made

S0-BIG-888

HEAVEN ON THURSDAY

"Voila - notre vie -
JESUS et rien que JESUS."
S. Madeleine Sophie

ST. MADELEINE SOPHIE BARAT

THE LIFE OF ST. MADELEINE SOPHIE BARAT

Heaven on Thursday

by M. K. RICHARDSON

THE NEWMAN PRESS

WESTMINSTER, MARYLAND

1949

NIHIL OBSTAT: IOANNES CAN. ARENDZEN, D.D., PH.D., M.A.
CENSOR DEPVTATVS
IMPRIMATVR: E. MORROGH BERNARD,
VICARIVS GENERALIS
WESTMONASTERII: DIE XXX MARTII MCMXLVIII

PREFACE

A FULL life of eighty-five years cannot be confined easily to the limits of a small book. In her lifetime there were many who looked upon Madeleine Sophie Barat as a saint, and, in view of her canonization, recorded their dealings with her. The great French work of Mgr. Baunard, which appeared in 1876, drew on the oral witness of numerous men and women who had known her. Mother Cahier, for many years her secretary, painstakingly amassed information from all her daughters, young and old, and in 1884 a detailed biography appeared. Much from these sources was used in the English *Life*, by Mother Margaret Ward, published in 1911. Mother Perdrau, the painter of "Mater Admirabilis," who lived for years at the school in the rue de Varenne in Paris in close proximity to St. Madeleine Sophie, had the artist's eye for more homely and less official situations, and set down the account of the day to day intimacy with her Mother Foundress, in her own easy, simple style, for the benefit of other generations of religious.[1] But in the early *Journal* of the first noviceship in Poitiers which St. Madeleine Sophie herself kept, in her many conferences to her daughters, and in thousands of letters[2] which she wrote to all kinds of people, she speaks for herself and makes known her attractive humility and all-embracing charity. With this wealth of material available, selection has been necessary, and while the sequence of her life-story has

[1] Some of her recollections have appeared in *Happy Memories of a Saint* (Sands).

[2] Fourteen thousand were examined during the process of her canonisation.

been preserved in this biography, incidents which focus on certain aspects of her character have been chosen.

With the exception of a few minor remarks, all the words put into the mouth of the Saint are her own, though some have been taken from their original context to do duty in a similar situation. Mother Perdrau's *Memories* provide the originals of most of the children. A few unimportant characters have been named where contemporary accounts only made known their existence.

In the first chapters, the name Sophie has been kept, since of her three baptismal names, Madeleine Louise Sophie, this was the one used by her family and her earliest intimates. As Mother General, she celebrated the Feast of St. Mary Magdalen as her name day, but she was known to all as Mother Barat.

The first steps towards her canonisation were taken in 1879 when the Cause was solemnly introduced in Paris. She was beatified by Pius X on May 24th, 1908, and canonised by Pius XI on May 24th, 1925. In his speech to the thousands of children, mothers and grandmothers, gathered in St. Peter's from all over the world, proudly claiming the title of children of St. Madeleine Sophie, the Holy Father spoke of his joy and gratitude in having been chosen in the mysterious designs of Providence to be the instrument of her glorification. "She comes to the aid of minds and hearts to set far from them that most terrible poverty of all—ignorance; and to pour into them the greatest, most abounding and most necessary of all wealth —Christian knowledge. Mother Barat has been faithful to her name of Sophie. . . . Wisdom showed itself in her by a union of strength and gentleness. To know what should be learnt, to know what should be done, there is wisdom, there is the secret of life." To-day more than ever, we need the Saint's wisdom to teach us how to live.

LIST OF CONTENTS

Chapter I

FIRE!

IT seemed to eleven-year-old Louis Barat that he had stood for hours at the garret window, watching the progress of the flames. When they first ran down the Rue Neuve crying out "Fire! Fire!" he would have been out of the house like a shot to see if he could be of any use to the men who were rushing out from the nearby houses with pails of water and plenty of shouted advice to the unfortunate family standing disconsolately in the street watching their home blazing fiercely in the blackness of the December night, but Jacques Barat had forbidden him, and Louis had learnt to recognise the note of authority in the voice of his kindly father, and knew that he must stay in the house.

"We may want you", the cooper said to his son; Louis then had run up to the garret and opened the window wide so that he could see and hear all the excitement in the town and stifle his regrets at not being able to lend a hand to the men who were doing their best to localise the outbreak and keep the fire from spreading to the other old timbered dwellings that leant up against it.

Presently his ten-year-old sister Marie-Louise crept in and knelt alongside of him, her face lit up by the red haze in the sky.

"Louis", she whispered in awed tones, "isn't it dreadful?" He thought a minute.

"It's frightening, Marie-Louise, because if it once gets a hold on things, you can't stop it."

"Do you think it'll reach our house?"

"I don't know—we'll have to pray God to stop it in time. But it's rather lovely all the same. Look at that."

A falling beam sent up a cascade of sparks that lit the whole sky. The clouds of smoke swirled round, eddied, caught the light of the flames, then steadied themselves like a great column stretching from the earth to the heavens.

"It's like God leading the Israelites", Louis mused. "It's burning steadily now. You must be able to see it for miles and miles."

"Do you think you'd see it the other side of the hills, Louis?"

"Well, I think you might."

"Right as far as Paris?"

"That's a long way for a fire to reach, but——"

"But you might just see a little light perhaps in the sky, Louis. Fancy Joigny lighting up the world like that!"

The door opened and Jacques Barat appeared. There was an air of anxiety about him and his eyes were troubled.

"Louis", he asked, "are you there?"

"Yes, Father, and Marie-Louise."

"Good. Now listen, children. God has given you a new little sister."

The boy and girl broke out into an exclamation of delight, but their father looked grave.

"She is so small, my dears, so very weak that—that we don't know if she will live. If God is calling her home to Him, we must make her a true little child of God. Louis, I want you to go off at once to St. Thibaud's and ask the priest if he will baptise her as soon as possible. We can't afford to wait."

"Yes, Father. I'll go at once."

"And you, Louis, can be the godfather. Madame Cédor says her daughter will act as godmother."

Louis hesitated.

"Well, Louis, what is it?"

"Could I just see the baby before I go?"

Their father led the children down the steep little stairs to the door of their mother's room. He knocked gently. In a moment fat, friendly Madame Cédor appeared with a little bundle in her arms. She beckoned to the two to come quietly and lifted back the shawl. Louis looked with surprise at the tiny pink face that was revealed.

"What wee fingers!" Marie-Louise whispered. "She doesn't look real." A faint cry came from the baby.

"Not real yourself", Madame Cédor said. "As fine a little creature as I've seen—only so small and weak. Louis, you be off on the errand your father's given you. And you, Marie-Louise, get down to your prayers. We don't want another little angel in heaven if we can help it."

Louis went through the family living room and unhooked his coat. The December night was cold. Jacques was waiting in his workshop among the barrels, and he opened the door into the little courtyard.

"Don't be gone long, son", he said, as Louis clattered across the flag-stones and out into the street.

The square church tower stood out against the dying redness of the burning house. Men were returning to their homes tired out with their exertions but satisfied that the danger was over. The curé had just reached his bed when there was a knock at his door. He had been wondering whether he would be able to get at least a couple of hours' sleep before the morning Mass, so he opened his window, and called down rather testily:

"Who's there?"

"Me, Father; Louis Barat."

"And what in the name of all the saints and angels do you want with me at this time of night?"

"My father sent me to ask if you would baptise my new little sister as soon as possible this morning; they think she is going to die."

The good priest forgot his annoyance.

"Bring her round as soon as you can. I shall be ready. Your mother's prayers will keep her alive at least until we've made her a true child of God. But what about sponsors?"

"Madame Cédor says her daughter will be godmother."

"But she wants a godfather."

"I'll be that, Father."

"You, Louis Barat? A boy of eleven like you?"

"Father, I'll be a good one, please God. She's so small— I'll look after her all right. You know I am going to be a priest, Father. I'll help her to get to heaven."

"H'mm. Well, don't you forget it's a grave responsibility to be a godfather."

The priest withdrew and shut his window with a slam. Louis turned and made his way back.

"I'll be a good godfather to her, if you'll let her live, dear God", he prayed. "I'll see that she loves You and works for You. I'll help her to be holy, if You'll keep her from dying, please."

In the east the dawn was beginning to flush everything with a vivid red that spread across the cold grey of the sky, reflecting against the massed clouds in the west.

"Like fire", Louis thought, and then unbidden there came into his head some words from the Gospel. "I came to cast fire on the earth——" Fire, fire. Dreadful and beautiful.

Chapter II

PLAY-TIME

I**T** was a very hot afternoon. Madame Foufé, who had determined to say the fifteen decades of the Rosary for the success of her grandson Louis Barat in the seminary of Sens, was peacefully nodding before the high altar, the beads wound firmly round her fingers. The flies buzzed; in the church tower the pigeons drowsily murmured, and the occasional soft whirring of their wings as they settled down only stirred the warm air to make its heat the more conscious. The catechism class was seated on benches by the open door through which a cat lazily rubbed her way to curl herself up in the security and shade of the last row. That was where the good children sat, or at least, those who could be trusted not to cause untoward disturbances. But even Paul in the front row right under the eyes of the priest was too listless to be a nuisance. He had stopped kicking Jean from sheer boredom and was now vacantly staring at the priest whose voice droned on and on—Jean was playing with a bit of string under his Sunday blouse. Antoinette was casting baleful looks at Cécile flaunting her mittens in spite of the weather, while Cécile in pretended indifference watched their effect. Heads were nodding, feet were shuffling—it was very hard to follow what the priest was saying. Under his shaggy eyebrows the good father looked at his little flock.

"Oh dear, oh dear", he thought, "what is the good of talking to them about the love of God—it is so vast and vague. If only I knew of a way to make them understand and realise that God loves them."

He leant forward and tapped Paul sharply on the knee. "Who made you?" he asked.

Paul shut his mouth and opened it, but no sound came. Jean kicked him under the bench.

"God", he prompted, and Paul got the answer out in time. The class moved, wriggling in their places. Questions —then the end was in sight. If only they knew the right replies!

"Why has God created you and put you in the world?"

There was an uneasy silence. No one wanted to catch the eye of the priest, while each hoped that someone else might remember the correct formula. The priest frowned.

"What? Can no one answer that simple question?"

Above the fidgeting of the children's feet, a little voice arose from the back row.

"Eh?" said the priest, cupping his hand round his ear. "I can't hear you, child. Stand up and speak out."

There was a protesting mew as a cat was put down from her warm refuge in a little girl's lap, and then the answer came clear.

"To know Him, to serve Him and to love Him, Father."

"Right, my child. But stand up on the bench so that I can see you properly. Oh, it's you, Sophie Barat. Well, do you serve God?"

"I say my prayers, Father, and my brother Louis says that if I help my mother, it's serving God."

"Very good. And do you know God?"

Sophie did not answer. The class grew anxious. Was Sophie going to let them down by not satisfying the priest? It would be their turn to be under fire then. How could they know that Sophie was puzzled?

"How can I say I know God?" she thought. "He's so

great—like an ocean stretching away and away—but then I do know something about Him."

"Here's a strange thing", the priest remarked. "Sophie Barat doesn't know if she knows God though she's eight years old. Well, my dear, do you love Him?"

"Oh, yes, Father", Sophie answered without a moment's hesitation.

"H'm, that's better. Now children, just think over this problem by next Sunday: is it more important to know God or to love Him?"

And with that he dismissed the class.

Jean was waiting for Sophie outside the church door, and caught her arm as she ran out.

"Sophie", he pleaded, "will you come and play with me? I've got a lovely new game to show you."

Antoinette was lingering near.

"Can I come too, Jean?" She put the question from force of habit, knowing well what her brother's answer would be.

"You, 'Toinette? I should say! Why, you know you can't run like Sophie. You'd never keep up."

Antoinette's lips trembled.

"But I want to know what your new game is." She twined her arm through Sophie's. "Ask him to let me come," she said coaxingly.

"Can't she come, Jean?" Sophie asked. "We needn't go too fast."

"Oh, all right", Jean conceded grudgingly, and then magnanimously, as he realised that Antoinette would be useful to them for beating the bushes, "All right, come on."

"Where are we going?" Sophie asked as the children crossed the bridge over the Yonne and clambered down into the meadows.

"Over there", Jean replied, pointing to a little thicket of trees and bushes. "I've got a new catapult. Look."

He drew it with pride from under his blouse.

"It shoots like anything. See that clump of hemlock over there? I bet I knock off the head of the tallest flower."

He picked up a stone and fitted it to the sling while the two girls admired in silence. Then with careful aim he sent the stone towards the hemlock. A shout of triumph—the large head hung broken on its stem.

"You *are* a good shot", Antoinette said. "What are you going to do now?"

"Well, I want you to go on and beat the bushes over there. Sophie is to stay with me because she'll bring me good luck. If you go behind that furze, you'll find there's a lark's nest somewhere near. Make a noise, 'Toinette, so's the bird gets on the wing."

Sophie's eyes grew round with horror.

"But, Jean, you're never going to shoot the larks?"

"Of course I am. Don't be silly, Sophie. It's great fun, and I can get money for them."

"Please, Jean, please don't shoot the birds."

"Oh don't bother me now. There's 'Toinette—she's found the place."

In a minute there was a sudden flutter from behind the furze bush, and a small bird rose into the air, hung for a moment with beating wings, then rose higher. Jean had his stone ready.

"Oh dear God", Sophie prayed with all her heart, "don't let him hit it."

The stone flashed forward.

"Bother!" Jean cried. "That was a rotten stone."

The lark was soaring up into the blue sky. Presently they could not see it.

"It's singing beautifully", Sophie said.

Jean was getting ready for another shot.

"There are some finches there. Make them rise, 'Toinette."

His sister dutifully obeyed, but Sophie was still praying.

"Please, God, make him miss, make him miss. Don't let him get a single one."

At the end of half an hour, Jean grew hot and cross.

"It's not my catapult that's wrong and you've seen how I can hit things—it's just bringing you silly girls with me. I'll never ask you to come again, Sophie. Come along. Let's get home again."

He thrust the sling into his pocket.

"I'll race you home, Sophie. You can have a start, 'Toinette."

Laughing and breathless, the boy and girl reached the bridge together. In the distance Antoinette was plodding along valiantly.

"We'll wait for her", Sophie said.

When she reached home, Marie-Louise greeted her at the door in the Rue du Puits-Chardon.

"Oh, there you are—come and see who's here."

Sophie took one look through the open door, then flung herself into the arms of her brother.

"Oh, Louis, how lovely to see you. And you've got the tonsure! Will you be a priest soon? Are you staying here long? Will you be able to come for walks with me? There are such a lot of things I want to ask you."

"And I can't answer all of them in one breath, Sophie. I'm only home on holiday, and it'll be some years before I'm ordained; and you'll have to pray hard, for there are a lot of men who don't want priests now. And there are lots of things I want to ask you. Is she being a help to you, Mother?"

Madame Barat smiled.

"Almost as good as Marie-Louise in the house, Louis, and far better than her if I want any reading done. She's a forward little scholar and makes a story interesting when she reads it."

B

Louis pondered.

"Do you like books, Sophie?" he asked.

"Oh, yes. They're so interesting. You can get to know such a lot from them." She stopped short as a sudden thought struck her. "Louis, can you get to know God from books?"

Louis laughed.

"It depends on the books, Sophie. Do you want to get to know God?"

Sophie nodded.

"Then I shall have to help you to find the right books."

Jacques Barat looked in admiration at his learned son.

"That's right, Louis, help your little sister. She's got her mother's brains."

"Sophie", Madame Barat called from the kitchen fire, "come and lend a hand with your brother's meal. You can watch this omelette for him."

Chapter III

SCHOOL-TIME

Louis was better than his word. In the years that followed he took his sister's education very much to heart and found a great many books for her—too many, Madame Barat sometimes thought when she would have liked to be chatting with her daughter of this and that and the other event in the life of Joigny. But Jacques Barat, growing daily more and more proud of his daughter's accomplishments, growled softly, "Leave them alone, Mother", whenever his wife complained that her son was making Sophie work too hard.

Louis, ordained deacon, had been sent back from Sens by his ecclesiastical superiors to teach Mathematics in the College at Joigny. It was a grand opportunity for teaching Sophie too.

"She's quick at seeing a point", he told the old parish priest. "She's got a good memory and she thinks about what she reads."

The old priest chuckled.

"I could have told you that, Louis Barat. Some of you go about with no eyes in your heads—or no brains behind your eyes. Why, last year my curate came to me with a long face. That little Barat child, he said, she wants to make her first Communion. Well? I said. She's too young to know much about things, he said. Fiddlesticks, I said to him. If you want a good, shrewd, theological answer to any question, she's the child to ask, and if you want a loving heart for Our Blessed Lord to rest in, you'll have to journey miles before you find a better. And what are you teaching her now, Louis?"

"Oh, I've started her on Latin and Greek; she does some mathematics and botany, French literature, of course, and some elementary astronomy."

"Not a bad programme. And how does she find the time?"

"I've given her a timetable—she gets up early when my father goes off to the vineyard, or down to his workshop, and goes to Mass. Then after her breakfast, she goes up to her room and gets on with her studies. Mother has let her have the garret—it's quiet and there aren't perpetual interruptions."

"Don't you let her have some pleasure, you hard-hearted schoolmaster?"

"Oh, yes, she's learning Italian—and she wants to begin on Spanish."

"And that's what you call pleasure?"

"Well, Father, I tell you you'd find Sophie as greedy for reading and learning as any student—perhaps too greedy."

"So you think that it's you who must put the brake on, eh?"

Louis nodded. He honestly thought his sister might forget she was living in a real world of men and women if she lived too much among her books.

He did not let Sophie know that she was making huge strides—that might flatter her vanity. He even felt a bit guilty himself at the feeling of pride that came over him when week after week he announced to his class of boys in the college:

"Here are your exercises back. Sophie has top marks again." But he justified the announcement by thinking what a spur to endeavour it was for his boys to be beaten by a girl—and a younger girl at that.

There were times off for Sophie. At the vintage season, Louis was generally at Sens and then what a glorious holiday there was among the vines, playing with the other children, laughing and talking and picnicking on the hillsides, watching the twisting Yonne shining in the sunlight. Golden days like this ought to last for ever—what part had ablative absolutes and deponent verbs and even botanical classifications in the happiness of chasing down the hills or filling the wicker baskets with the grapes?

"It's right that the child should have as many days off as she can", Madame Barat was thinking one day, when a shadow fell across the open door and her son walked in.

"Louis, what are you doing here? I thought you were at Sens." Madame Barat tried not to sound annoyed.

"No, Mother, I finished my work there so I came back. I'd like to put in some time with Sophie. I'll just run upstairs."

"Louis", Madame Barat stopped him with her hand on his sleeve, playing for time, "I declare, you are almost threadbare. Sit down here and I'll mend that sleeve for you immediately."

"Thank you, Mother." Louis slipped his coat off. "Here you are. I'll just go up to the garret while you're doing it."

"Well, Louis", his mother was at bay now, "you can go up, but you won't find Sophie there. I sent her out. It's ridiculous keeping her nose in books every day."

"But, Mother, she's had her holidays. She ought to be back at work again. Where is she?"

"Where should she be but out playing with the other children in the vineyard? Where are you off to now, Louis?"

Louis had put on his coat again and was making for the door.

"I'm going to bring her back", he said quietly, and was out before Madame Barat could protest further.

Louis' scolding was not eloquent but it was effective. Sophie put down her basket half-filled with grapes and turned homewards. She did not offer any excuse—after all, she ought to have been at her books—and the tears in her eyes were more for having displeased the beloved brother who had done so much for her than for the good time foregone. Her tiny pet lamb followed her in and she caught her up in her arms and found comfort in the trustful response to her hug. As she climbed up the garret stairs, with her cheek pressed against the woolly head, her mother was upbraiding Louis.

"Why can't you let her have some little pleasure? What good is all this learning going to do her? A fine housewife like Sophie will soon get a good husband and then where's your Latin and Greek?"

Sophie didn't catch her brother's answer. Another truth was filling her mind.

"It's true, then", she thought sadly, "there's no pleasure without bitterness."

She looked out of the garret window. The happy shouts of the other children came to her and she saw the blue sky and the green valley. Then she opened her copy of *Virgil*, and began translating. Soon the voices outside ceased to trouble her; instead the cry of the Sybil sounded in her ears, and she stood with Æneas by the gloomy flood watching Charon, and the ghosts of the mighty ones of old thronged round her—hero and poet and priest—and the sunlit hills of Burgundy became a dream as she saw the weary dead stretching out their hands in vain for the further shore. A cool wet muzzle was rubbed against her knee, but she only glanced down for a moment at her pet lamb who, quite content, settled herself at her feet. For now old Anchises was rehearsing the grandeur that would be Rome's, king and emperor succeeding each other until the vision came that showed the hope of all Rome's greatness lying dead, strewn with fragrant lilies and the purple roses of spring, and poor Augustus mourned the young Marcellus, the whole world in his hands and his son dead before him—tears were at the very heart of things. Sophie looked up. Louis stood in the doorway, quietly watching his sister with the pile of books before her and the little white ball of wool at her side. He put his finger to his lips.

"Look at your lamb, Sophie. How happy she is!"

"What is she doing, Louis?"

"Don't you see what she's doing? She's loving."

So that was what gave happiness. It was a good thing to know.

"*Felix qui potuit rerum cognoscere causas.*" Yes, *Virgil* was right. It was a blessedness to understand the causes of things—but supposing the Roman poet had written *causam* instead.

"How would you translate that, then, Sophie?" Louis queried.

"Happy is he who can understand the Cause of things—who can know God."

"Quite right. And then you would be able to lie at His feet like your pet lamb, and just love the Good Shepherd."

The lamb nuzzled softly against her knee, as Louis went downstairs again.

Chapter IV

TEMPERING

WHEN Sophie was thirteen, Marie-Louise got married. Madame Barat was pleased to have a sound business man like M. Dusaussoy for her son-in-law and Jacques Barat welcomed so sensible a man and a good Christian at that. There was only one fly in the ointment.

"I am sorry that Louis isn't yet ordained", said Marie-Louise. "I should have liked him to say the Nuptial Mass, but never mind—the troubles will be over soon, and when the old times come again, he'll be a priest—in time to marry you, Sophie."

Her father shook his head.

"I don't think so. These changes in the Constitution—all this talk about the rights of man—the King not his own master—so much unrest even in the provinces—these outbreaks of violence—they are changing the face of France—it'll be a long time before things are the same again."

Sophie was shaking her head too.

"I don't want Louis to marry me."

"Why not?" asked Marie-Louise, turning the bright, new gold ring on her finger and smiling.

"Because I am going to be a nun."

"A nun? Whatever for? Why, you don't even know what a nun is."

"I do. It's someone who has promised to serve God all the days of her life—for better, for worse—just like you have promised your husband."

"But you've never even seen a nun——"

"She's not likely to see one now," her father put in. "These last two years they've closed all the convents and monasteries."

"And where are the nuns?" Marie-Louise asked.

"Most of them in prison—those that couldn't escape abroad", Louis told her. Then as the two sisters went to help their mother, he turned with a serious face to his father.

"I wanted to speak to you, Father, about the Civil Constitution of the clergy—when I put my name to the oath to accept it——"

"What are you worrying over that for now, son?" Jacques Barat asked. "It wasn't your fault that you signed it—how could you know it was wrong when your own Archbishop set you the example? Besides, you retracted all that."

"Oh, I'm not bothering about my deed—the civil authorities know quite well—I couldn't have put it more plainly in my letter to them—that I acknowledge that my priestly mission comes from the Church of God alone and not from the State—but it's that very plainness that makes me now a marked man. The outcry against the clergy has spread from Paris all through the country and now even in Joigny there are men saying—'Take the oath to the State or—death!' "

"What do you think you had better do, Louis? Your mother would die if you came to any harm."

"I think there is safety in numbers. Here everyone knows me. In Paris, I should be lost in the crowd."

"But Paris is the hotbed of all the trouble."

"But an unknown Burgundian could pick up a living there without exciting suspicion."

So Louis went off to Paris and Marie-Louise went off to

her own well-appointed house, and Sophie stayed to be the comfort of her mother. Madame Barat clung more and more to her little daughter as the news from the capital grew worse, and the September Massacres reddened the prisons, and the king himself was guillotined.

Then one day a traveller came along the Rue du Puits-Chardon inquiring where the Barat family lived. Arrived at the door, he asked to see Jacques Barat. Sophie set a chair for him and went to the workshop to call her father, while Madame Barat, hearing voices, came downstairs.

"We are alone, I hope?" the man asked, settling himself by the table after carefully closing the door.

"Quite", the cooper assured him. "What do you want?"

"I come from Louis Barat——"

"Ha! A friend of my son's must have good entertainment." Jacques was off to the cellar and came back at once with a bottle of wine. "My own vintage", he said proudly, as he took out the cork.

"Wait", said the man. "I must give you my message first."

Jacques' gnarled fingers trembled, and the wine overflowed the glass.

"What is it?" he asked.

"He's dead!" Madame Barat cried, and Sophie put her arm round her.

"No, Madame", said the man, relieved that he could soften the blow. "Not dead, but in prison."

Madame Barat burst into tears. Jacques looked inquiringly at the stranger, not trusting himself to speak.

"He was going along the street one day, when he heard someone shout his name. He turned and a man ran up. 'Why, it is you, Louis Barat. I thought I recognised you. Don't you remember me—Philippe Caussade, who used to sit on the same bench as you at the College in Joigny?' Your son was pleased to see an old school friend, and asked him to his lodgings and made him at home. 'So you're determined to be a priest?' Philippe asked as he went away, and Louis said he was. The man went straight to the Committee of Public Safety and denounced him. The soldiers came for him while I was in the house, and while they finished a bottle of wine, he asked me to try to let you know and to give you these with his love."

He slipped off the dusty haversack from his shoulders and rummaged inside. Then he pulled out two pictures and spread them on the table.

"Our Blessed Lady", Sophie said, looking at the first. "Mother, see the sword that is piercing her heart—she knows all about a mother's pain."

"And the other is Our Lord", Madame Barat picked it up as she spoke. "It's a beautiful print—but He is showing His Sacred Heart surrounded with a crown of thorns and with flames coming from it. My mother would never let us have a picture like that—a new-fangled devotion she called it."

"Mother", Jacques Barat's tone was final, "we are going to put those two pictures up here—over the fireplace would be a good spot for them."

The traveller looked alarmed.

"That's a risky thing to do", he said. "If they search the house, those pictures will give you away. They're anathema to our revolutionary citizens."

"If my son can brave prison for his faith, I think we can run a little risk here", said the cooper quietly. "But they'll go there to remind us to pray for him. Our Lord can keep him safe if it is His Will. I'm not a scholar like you, Mother, and Sophie, but I do remember that Our Lord promised Margaret Mary Alacoque that He would watch over the house where an image of His Sacred Heart was honoured."

The traveller slipped on his haversack again, picked up his staff, and rose to go.

"Well, I'll be off now. I'm glad to have been able to do something for Louis. He's a good man and has helped me a lot."

"We can never thank you enough", Jacques answered him. "Where are you going now?"

"Where indeed?" asked the man. "To Switzerland—perhaps to Italy. It's hard to find any country in Europe that's free from revolution. Perhaps I'll go in the end to America—they say that in the States a man may worship as he pleases. I'd rather keep my head on my shoulders. You can't pray without a head, can you, Mademoiselle?"

And with that he was gone.

The weeks that followed were anxious ones. Each courier from Paris brought ill news. The toll of victims claimed by Madame la Guillotine rose day by day until nearly two hundred were killed weekly. Madame Barat gave up all hope. She sat listlessly in her chair and wept all day, and resolutely refused to see any comfort.

"Sophie", said her father coming in one day, and showing her a bright silver fish, "I got this from old Père Martin as he came up from the river. Couldn't you cook it in an appetising way—make a good tasty sauce—garnish it with parsley—and tempt your mother to eat it? She's not eaten for the last two weeks and she's getting thinner and thinner."

Sophie took the fish.

"I'll do my best", she replied, "but you know, she wouldn't touch the chicken you got her yesterday. She'll die if we can't manage to make her take some nourishment."

When the meal time came round, Sophie set the dish before her mother. It smelt good, thought the cooper—nothing wrong with Sophie's cooking. Madame Barat took up the dish without glancing at it and set it down in front of her daughter. Sophie picked it up and set it down in front of her father.

"I won't eat any more", she said in a determined voice. Her mother broke her gloomy silence.

"Are you ill, Sophie?"

"No, Mother. But I've decided not to eat anything as long as you don't eat. At least we can die together."

Madame Barat looked at Sophie. There was no mistaking her resolution.

"Take just a little bit to please me."

"No, Mother."

Madame Barat burst into tears. Then she rose and came and put her arms round Sophie.

"If you'll have a little helping, I will too", she conceded.

Sophie served some of the fish on to a plate, set it in front of her mother, and took a little herself. Madame Barat began her meal. When the plates were empty, Sophie got up to clear them away. Her eyes caught those of her father and twinkled.

"There are some fine plums here", she said, and put a dish in front of her mother. Madame Barat took one without a protest.

When the meal was over and the cooper had persuaded his wife to accompany him to the vineyard, Sophie stood a long time in front of the pictures over the mantelpiece.

"O Lord Jesus," she prayed, "I confide Louis to You. Only look at him in his prison and then do what Your Heart inspires. I count on it, I trust in it."

Shut up first in the Conciergerie, Louis was taken from prison to prison till he reached that of St. Lazare. It was a motley collection he found in the great, bare, stone dungeon: aristocrats and commoners, soldiers and priests.

"You are a deacon already?" his fellow prisoner the Abbé Duclaux asked him. "In that case we could continue your theological studies for the priesthood together. We shall have plenty of time, and few interruptions, and it seems a pity to waste the opportunity. Even if an inevitable

interruption should terminate our studies, the extra knowledge we have gained of God will have honoured Him."

At that moment the door was unbolted and the gaoler
appeared. He was a big swarthy fellow and he glowered
round the room.

"Wanted for the tumbrils' free ride to-day", he shouted,
laughing at his own joke, "the following citizens—Tesseire,
Closset, Caillaux, and de la Taille. Sorry to disappoint the
rest of you."

The four came forward but at the door the old priest
Abbé Closset turned.

"Pray for us, friends", he said simply.

Louis fell on his knees.

"Bless us, Father", he begged, and the old man raised his
hand in a last benediction.

"Come on", said the gaoler, pushing past the kneeling
Louis. "You, citizen, need not be anxious that you'll not
see Paris again—the view's quite good from the Republic's
carriage. Only have a little patience. Your turn will come",
and he hustled out his victims and slammed the door.

In the private room of the governor, Citizen Moreau was
standing awaiting his orders.

"Look here," the governor pointed to a pile of papers
in front of him, "I don't know what they think I am—a
clerk, I suppose, to keep all these records and lists. Well, I
just can't turn myself into a pen-pushing notary, so I want
you to find one of the prisoners that can do a copying job
for me and keep these lists of executions from day to day.
I won't have any priest—I'd sooner do the work myself
than save one of their rascally heads. I suppose you don't
write yourself?"

Citizen Moreau shook his head.

"Ah, well", the governor shrugged his shoulders. "Do
your best, but mind, not a priest."

Citizen Moreau took the keys and went the rounds.

"Not that room", he said as he passed the dungeon where Louis was, "it's full of priests. Now I might be lucky here."

So saying he unlocked a heavy door and thrust his head into a room where a babel of sound greeted him. He yelled for silence.

"Is there anyone here who knows how to write?" he asked.

"What do you take us for, a lot of aristocrats?" a ragged man sneered at him.

"Is there no one here? Speak up, can't you?"

In the far corner a man who was busy playing cards laid down his hand, and cried out "I can."

"Good old Jerome! The pen is mightier than the sword!" his companions clapped him on the back. "Set him an exercise of pothooks and hangers, Citizen Moreau—he's trying it on with you."

Citizen Moreau glared at him.

"You're a soldier, here for disloyalty to the Republic— and you pretend to be able to write?"

"It happens to be true. Before I was a soldier, I taught in a school, quite a good one, too", he added with a grin at his surprised friends. "It was in a little town in Burgundy— Joigny was the name, if you want to verify my statement."

"All right, you'll do", Citizen Moreau grunted and led him to the little cell where table, pen, paper and ink were provided, and he was shown his daily task of copying out the names sent from the tribunals, of those who were to be executed.

"We'll keep him on this job", the governor said. "He's a lovely hand-writing."

Jerome Giraud did not object. A bit of a philosopher, he found it interesting to speculate on the names and possible histories of those whom he was passing on to death through the movement of his pen on the white paper. One day a name set memory working.

"Louis Barat", he mused. "Knew a Louis Barat once—
a bright little fellow—top of his class in the College of
Joigny—yes, I remember what a treat it was to teach him—
I wonder where he is now—hardly here in Paris. Still, for
old association's sake——"

He dipped his pen, looked at the next name on the
condemned list, and wrote that instead.

And so it came about that though eighty-five prisoners
went from that prison to the scaffold in that fateful year,
Louis Barat was not among them.

"I know it's a risk", thought Jerome, "but it pleases me
to go back to those pleasant peaceful times, and so, good
luck to the bearer of the name of Louis Barat."

The July sun was turning the streets of Joigny into a
furnace when the Paris coach came lumbering in in a cloud
of dust. The driver could scarcely wait to descend before
he gave his news.

"Robespierre has fallen!"

"What? Robespierre? The man responsible for the
reign of terror in the capital?" The news spread quickly.

"It's true", the passengers affirmed. "His head has gone
into the same basket as other men's and women's."

"Hi! Do you hear that, Jacques Barat?" The innkeeper
called to the cooper who was passing. "Robespierre is dead.
Things will change now, mark my words."

Jacques Barat almost ran home to give the news to his
wife.

"And will Louis be free now?" Sophie questioned him
eagerly.

"Not at once, I shouldn't think, but soon, please God."

"Is anything difficult to Me? saith the Lord", Sophie
thought as she turned to the picture over the fireplace.

"O Sacred Heart of Jesus, I have trusted in You."

Chapter V

IF A THING'S WORTH DOING...

Louis was released from prison along with many other fortunate people. As soon as it was possible he was ordained in secret in Paris, but there were no churches open yet for him to work in. He had been so close to death for so many months that he had learnt how valuable life is, and was bent on not wasting one precious moment of his life. But what could he do? He longed ardently to be a Jesuit, and fight in the ranks of St. Ignatius' army for Christ the King, but the Jesuits had been driven out of every country in Europe, and if he went to Russia to join them, he would not be able to work for his beloved France where so many were indifferent to religion, so many actively hostile, so many now growing up knowing nothing of God and interested only in having a good time. He was puzzled, but the holy Abbé Duclaux had taught him, not only the science of theology, but also the art of prayer, not only to know about God, but to know God, so he entrusted his problem to Him, and set about the work that lay ready to his hand.

When he went back to Joigny, he noticed a great change in his little sister. She had grown up. She still laughed and sang merrily as she went quickly and deftly about the household tasks, but there was a deeper note in her voice and though her quick wit flashed out in kindly humorous sallies, there was a real underlying seriousness and steadiness that made everyone turn to her for help and advice—her mother, her father, Marie-Louise had got into the habit of relying on her, M. Dusaussoy was not slow to ask her opinion in business matters, while baby Stanislaus was never so gurglingly content as when Auntie Sophie had him on her lap.

But Louis was worried. Sophie's praises were being sung by everyone. She was being treated as if she were the daughter of a prince and not of a poor cooper in a small town in a French province. She had but to express a wish and the tender love of her father and her mother would try to supply it. Frankly, she was being spoilt. Admiration and overflowing love—were these the right soil for holiness to grow in? And nothing short of holiness would content Louis when he thought of all the gifts of heart and head God seemed to have given Sophie. So he asked that his sister should come back to Paris with him. His proposal met with a blank refusal from Jacques and his wife and Sophie herself. The idea was preposterous. Louis went back to the capital alone.

"But I know I'm right", he told himself. "I won't give up my plan. They can think me hard-hearted and too thorough in my treatment of Sophie, but if a thing's worth doing, it's worth doing properly."

When he next returned to Joigny, he opened the question again. Sophie burst into tears.

"I've told you over and over again, it's against the law of nature to take a daughter from her mother", she said.

"My brother-in-law has taken Marie-Louise", Louis countered drily.

"It's against charity," Sophie retorted.

"It's not as if your mother were aged and ailing", Louis pointed out. "She doesn't really need you here, and if you follow God's plans for you, you will have the right to call upon the charity of God to help your mother."

"I won't be separated from Sophie", Madame Barat answered with finality. "Fancy my allowing a young girl of sixteen to go to Paris alone—what do you take me for, Louis?"

"But she won't be alone. I shall look after her, and she will live with me at Mlle. Duval's."

"Don't let him take me from you, Mother," Sophie put in.

"As if I should, my darling," Madame Barat reassured her.

Jacques Barat was sitting before the fire, listening in silence to the altercations. He looked at his wife and children, glanced at the pictures above the fireplace, shifted uneasily in his chair, then suddenly broke in.

"Louis is right, you know. Sophie is wasting her time here with us. She'll be quite safe in Paris with Louis, and she'll be able to go on with her studies. Mother, people there will understand her abilities better than here—she'll be able to make a better match there than in Joigny."

"Never", said Sophie decidedly, but Madame Barat began to let herself see another side to the situation.

"It isn't as if she's going for good", Louis pressed home his advantage. "She can come home for holidays at vintage time. She'll love Mlle. Duval—she's a grand old lady— she's turned one of her rooms into a chapel where we can say Mass in secret. You'll like the chapel, Sophie. It's got a picture of St. Ignatius and his first companions consecrating themselves to God in the church of Montmartre, and another beautiful one of the Holy Child clambering up on Our Lady's knee and pressing His face against hers while they both look out at the world as though each asked us to admire the other."

"And will Sophie have to help in the house?" Madame Barat asked.

"Wouldn't you want her to, Mother? But don't worry, there's Marguerite, Mlle. Duval's maid, who does all the heavy work."

"And who else is she likely to meet?" Jacques inquired.

"Well, there are a good many young women who come for instruction to Mlle. Duval's, because they want to do something for Our Lord, and I am teaching them and helping them to study. There's Mlle. Loquet, who runs a workshop for poor girls and writes books, and Mlle. Octavie Bailly, who has been hiding priests and getting the Last Sacraments for the dying, and preparing children for their first Communion all these years of the terror."

Sophie was silent. Were others to be heroes in God's service and was she just a coward? She, too, began to see another side to the situation.

So at length it was arranged, and Sophie, Louis and Stephanie Martin, who was going to join relations in Paris, set off from Joigny in the lumbering old stage coach.

On the third day, Sophie pointed excitedly through the window.

"Look, Stephanie, over there! Those must be the roofs and spires of Paris in the distance."

"You're right. Oh, Sophie, isn't it marvellous to be going to Paris—what a lot we'll have to see!"

"I wonder which are the towers of Notre Dame—perhaps you can't see it from here." Sophie craned her head to look.

"I wonder if we go past the Royal Palace—or if we shall see any of the shops? They say the Paris shops beat anything in Joigny."

"Perhaps we shall——" Sophie began, but Louis leant across and touched her knee.

"Sophie", he said severely, "is this the way to behave when you are just going into a town still red with the blood of martyrs, where the worship of God is still proscribed? I should have thought silence and prayer would have been more seemly."

Stephanie shrugged her shoulders, and laughed uncomfortably.

"Your brother's been a spoil-sport ever since we left home", she murmured to Sophie, but her companion did not answer. Tears filled her eyes at the thought of her thoughtlessness. It was not to have a good time that she was coming to this training ground of saints. Poor Sophie! But Louis would not say a word to soften his rebuke.

As time wore on, Sophie's life shaped itself into a definite pattern: study and work and teaching and praying, and then the joyous reunion in Joigny when the grapes were ripe on the hillsides.

She was sitting in Mlle. Duval's parlour one day opposite a little girl, whose neat appearance and carefully chosen dress in spite of signs of wear showed that her mother had seen better days, when the child sat back in her chair and asked:

"Where is the pretty dress you were making for yourself the other day, Mlle. Sophie?"

Sophie coloured.

"Laure, we ought to finish this lesson before we have a chat."

"Oh, but, Mlle. Sophie, you're blushing. I think you don't want to tell me. Where is it?"

"Where my vanity ought to be, Laure—in the fire."

"What! Who put it there? You won't say? Well, I can guess—it was that brother of yours. I'm glad I haven't a brother."

"Laure, you mustn't speak like that. You would be so grateful to some one who saw how vain you were. . . ."

Laure puckered her shrewd young face.

"It must be dreadful to be as vain as you, Mlle. Sophie. You should just see me on Sundays in the parks. Mother says, 'Ah, wait until things get better still and we have all

our property again. Then we'll be able to dress fashion-
ably.' But what a waste of a good dress—to burn it!"

"Better it than me, Laure. It's like what the Gospel tells
you to do with your eye or your hand if they offend."

Laure pouted.

"You know a Bible answer to everything." She was
silent, then added, "All the same, I think I'm glad you're
still wearing your Burgundian dress. It's quaint—it makes
me think of the country. When you go out in that little
frilled bonnet and your shawl, no one could take you for a
great lady."

"I'm not", Sophie said hurriedly.

"I mean", Laure explained herself, "I'd not be afraid to
tell you anything—even silly things."

She settled down to her task, but not for long.

"Mlle. Sophie", she asked, pushing her books away,
"why do we have to learn Latin?"

"So many great poets and philosophers wrote in Latin,
and you'll like to read their works."

"Do you read them?"

"I used to, but not now."

"What do you read now?"

"Well, you see, Latin is the language of the Church too
and I like to read St. Augustine and St. Ambrose and the
great Fathers of the Church——"

"And the Bible, Mlle. Sophie? Isn't that the best book
of all?"

"Quite the best, Laure. It has lots of wise things in
it."

"Tell me some."

"*Vade ad formicam, O piger, et considera vias eius et disce
sapientiam.*"

"Oh, but what does that mean?"

Sophie smiled.

"Go to the ant, thou sluggard, and consider her ways

and be wise", she translated and Laure took the hint. When the lesson was over, the little girl put on her hat and coat and then threw her arms round her teacher.

"Oh, Mlle. Sophie, I do love you. You make me feel so good inside."

Then she ran from the room.

Marguerite appeared at the door, wiping her hands on her apron.

"Your brother wants you", she said. "He's up in his room."

Sophie climbed the stairs, and went to the small attic that was Louis' room. A fire was burning in the hearth and the priest stood beside it.

"Ah, there you are. I have some good news for you", he told his sister. "Mlle. Loquet can let us use her workroom for a catechism class on Sundays, so you will be able to teach all the little ragamuffins of the district that I've collected for you."

"Oh, Louis, how splendid. We can start straight away to tell them about God and His goodness."

"Yes, this very Sunday. And you may fast properly all through this Lent and take the discipline every day as you have asked me."

Sophie smiled her gratitude.

"Are you still wearing that iron chain as a girdle?"

"Yes, Louis."

"Well, you may go on. And you may sleep on the floor as often as you want to."

"Oh, Louis, thank you. I wish——"

"What?"

"Oh, I do so wish there was a Carmelite convent I could go to."

"What for, Sophie?"

"I'd be a lay-sister and live a life alone with God, loving Him and doing penance."

"And what about my ragamuffins and their instruction?"

"Oh, Louis, I'm torn both ways. You are lucky to be a man . . . I do envy you."

"Why?"

"Because men can do great things for God."

"You'll never be a great saint, Sophie."

"No, Louis, great saints make me afraid. But at least I'll be like them in humility."

She turned and went to the door. She had her hand on the handle when Louis called her. He was holding up a parcel, the ribbon round which he had undone.

"Do you know anything about this, Sophie?"

"Yes, it was a surprise for you, Louis. I thought you would like a new shirt."

"And when did you make it?"

"I sat up at night", Sophie said, smiling in recollection of the pleasure making something for her brother had given her and thinking what care she had put into the stitching—it really was a fine piece of work.

"And who gave you permission to stay up?"

"No one, Louis. I thought——"

Louis threw the parcel on the fire. The paper caught, flared up, and in a moment the shirt was smouldering too.

"Understand, Sophie, that obedience is better than sacrifice. Now go down. I am off to see Father Varin."

Sophie kept back her tears until she reached the little room that was their chapel, and there she knelt before the tabernacle and sobbed and sobbed.

"Oh Jesus", she prayed, "I can't help crying—I'm not like the great saints. What is wrong with me? My brother is kind to everybody else, but he's always hard on me. Well, I'm sorry—help me to correct my faults. But I did think he'd like that shirt."

And her tears broke out afresh.

Chapter VI

WAITING FOR GOD'S HOUR

IN the spring and early summer of 1800, Louis Barat's acquaintance with Father Joseph Varin ripened into something more than friendship. It was an inspiration to see the young Superior of the Fathers of the Faith striding along the Paris streets, always calm and always gay, on his way to the Hospital of the Salpêtrière, where it needed physical courage to face the filth and squalor of hundreds of sick men and women, and an unwearying faith to try to teach them about a God whose name they only used as an oath. Few people could resist his victorious humility, and when Louis found that the Fathers of the Faith were only waiting until the Society of Jesus should be allowed to return to France to join it, he felt that his own goal was in sight.

When Sophie was spending her holiday in Joigny, he asked to be admitted to their company, and was received with joy. He was delighted with the poverty of their house.

"I like this community room", he said to Father Varin as the two were seated on the edge of a low couch that served as a bed.

"Community room!" laughed Father Varin. "You might as well call it dormitory or study-room or refectory——"

"Or kitchen or parlour", Louis finished for him. "That's why I like it—it's poor."

"I am glad you appreciate that—it makes me think you are going to be a true son of St. Ignatius. But tell me, have you no ties that still bind you to the world?"

Louis hesitated.

"I have a little sister", he said.

Father Varin turned to him, his face wearing an expression of eager delight that Louis could not fathom. To Father Varin, it seemed that the simple statement had set ajar a door that had long been shut.

"What is she like?" he asked, and waited as though expecting a revelation.

"She's nearly twenty", Louis told him. "She has learnt Latin and Greek, and she would make a good rhetorician with a sound grasp of philosophy. She hopes now to enter a convent—perhaps a Carmelite one."

Father Varin was silent for a long time, then he burst out:

"What fools we are to mistrust God—to think His ways could be mistaken. If only we had confidence and patience to wait for the striking of His hour. Listen, Louis, I have never told you much about myself——"

"I know you are a D'Ainvelle of Besançon", Louis put in.

"Well, if you would appreciate the patient working of God, you will have to hear more about me. I had a happy childhood—you should see the mountains and breathe their clean cold air, then you'd understand how I grew up so wildly fond of adventures and journeys and hunting— at sixteen, horses and dogs were all my delight. But my mother—she was a wonderful woman, Louis—was praying for me, so one day when I was nineteen I startled all my friends by betaking myself to St. Sulpice to study for the priesthood. They had the laugh on me when three years later they heard I had left the seminary and had joined the army of Condé. It wasn't that I couldn't do the studies or that my professors weren't pleased with me—the truth is, Louis, I couldn't sit still for long enough when I'd been up and doing all my life. I followed Condé in the campaigns of 1792 and '93, and my mother's prayers followed me. She was sure I had not found my vocation as a soldier.

"You can imagine how profoundly disgusted I was when I missed a great battle by being on leave when it was fought. Still dreaming of glory, I got permission to go north to Belgium to join the Hussards of Choiseul. Going through Venloo, I heard myself hailed, and there were four of my old friends of the seminary, all priests now. You'd think a soldier would be a bit of a fish out of water with them, but they pressed me to stay, and as Léonor de Tournély was one, I didn't need much persuasion. I wish you could have met him, Louis. I never saw a man so burning with the love of God—burning is the right word for it. Well, we talked of this and that, and then de Tournély suddenly asked me to join them and to consecrate myself like them to the service of God. You can guess how I laughed—to throw up my military career—'Do what you like with me, but don't make me a monk', I said. 'Don't get worried', de Tournély answered me; 'you will be a soldier still if you join us.' I pooh-poohed the whole idea, but to please them, I made my confession and received Holy Communion. Louis, I can't explain the change that came over me as I received Our Blessed Lord. I knew I must join them. An angel come express from Heaven couldn't have made me more sure."

Father Varin stopped, looking back into the past. Then he went on with an awed softness in his voice.

"Louis, I did not know it at the time, but they had put my mother into prison because she had corresponded with me, her emigré son. She would not deny the charge. 'I should offend God', she told her accusers, 'if I betray the truth and I do not want to do that any more than I wish to betray my Faith'. They condemned her to the guillotine. 'Don't let's complain', she remarked to her friends who were weeping around her. 'We know where we are going: first to the scaffold and then to Heaven.' Her last day on earth was the very day I saw God's Will in my regard.

"Others joined us", Father Varin continued, "and we went from country to country, till at length we found a haven in the hills near Vienna. We called ourselves the Fathers of the Sacred Heart then, and our one idea was to make Our Lord's love better known among men, and so bring them back again to God. I wish I could tell you more about our beloved Superior, Léonor. He was so close to God in prayer. It was in prayer that Our Lord first made known to him His desire to have a society of women consecrated to His Sacred Heart, who, by their prayer, should make reparation to His neglected love, and by their instruction of children should lead many souls to Him."

"What kind of children did He want them to teach?" asked Louis, thinking of Sophie's joy in gathering his little ragamuffins about her. "Poor children?"

"All poor children", Father Varin replied, thinking of the intellectual training Louis had given his sister; "the poor in this world's goods, and the wealthy ones of this world who are often so poor in the treasures of the world to come. When de Tournély met the Princess de Bourbon-Condé, he thought he had found the foundation stone of this new house of God—he was mistaken. The Princess entered the Trappistines after a short time, and the religious who had gathered around her dispersed. We thought he had been wrong in thinking God wanted this work when it came to grief so soon, and I said so plainly to him one day when we were walking up the hill towards our house. He looked at me and said, 'My friend, I thought that God wanted this foundation. Well, I still think it.' He lifted his head and his face glowed. 'God wants it', he cried like a prophet. 'I have just put out the first spark, but it will rekindle and flame up one day. I can make mistakes about the time and the means which the Lord has chosen for this society, but it will exist!' "

"And now Father de Tournély is dead", Louis commented, "and his work ended."

"No!" Father Varin's tone was strong. "You should have seen him die, Louis, and you would have said, 'Not ended, but begun.' The doctors said he died of small-pox; but it was the fire of his love of God that burned out the last shreds of his life. We felt he was going to a fuller existence, not to death. At the end, he called for me: 'Joseph', he said, 'I have confided everything to you. Go, but don't rush things. Wait for the moment of the Lord.' Then after a pause, on the very threshold of eternity, we heard him saying over and over again, 'It will be founded, it will be founded.' "

Father Varin paused and Louis wondered if he had finished. Then he said, "I, too, have been mistaken. I thought that the Archduchess Marie-Anne was the instrument to use, but she was not. I have been in the dark, waiting for God to show me. I think His moment has come. Louis, may I see your little sister when she comes back from Burgundy?"

So at the end of July, Father Varin presented himself at Mlle. Duval's and asked to see Mlle. Barat. It was an entirely unsuspecting and unprepared Sophie who turned the handle of the parlour door, plucking up courage to talk to a formidable stranger. And it was an entirely unprepared Father Varin who glanced up to see a small, frail girl, neatly dressed in the costume of a Burgundian peasant woman, standing timidly before him.

"What a foundation stone!" he thought, and then the door that had been set ajar when Louis first mentioned his sister, was flung wide. He could not doubt now that

God's hour was striking. But Sophie, he saw, was not ready yet. "Louis", he told her brother, "it's a good thing I have come along—you are killing your sister with your training".

"She can stand it", Louis said.

"She has stood it", Father Varin corrected. "But she's had enough of it."

"The sculptor gives pure marble many a hard blow when he wants to make a fine work of art", Louis pointed out.

"Right, Louis, but you are not dealing with marble. Your sister's soul is much more like a delicate, sensitive musical instrument—you will spoil the notes if you handle it too roughly."

Sophie soon learnt to love and trust Father Varin. At length, he told her of de Tournély and the work God seemed to want.

"I'll think about it", she said, overwhelmed at the idea of her own insufficiency to do anything to help the work of God.

"You will do nothing of the sort. When God speaks, you obey", said Father Varin with an assurance that brooked no denial.

Chapter VII

ON TIPTOE IN THE DARK

WHEN Sophie had agreed to be used by God in any way He chose in the foundation of a new society, Mlle. Loquet and Octavie Bailly wished to join in the enterprise. Each morning after Mass they would meet Father Varin to talk over their ideas and receive his instructions. Marguerite managed to get her household tasks done and come to listen too. "It is a grand thing", she thought, "to have brains. There is Mlle. Loquet, whom everyone knows and admires as a clever writer of books—though I never understand what they're about—and Mlle. Barat, who can teach Latin and Greek, and Mlle. Bailly, who can pray for hours on end out of her Office book. Well, well, they'll want their meals, and I suppose someone will have to sweep the rooms when they're busy with classes. I shan't have to be frightfully clever to do jobs like that."

So Marguerite asked if she might join.

Father Varin was delighted. A lay sister who loved God and who saw that all work was equal in value if it was done in His service was a true gift of God.

"What ought to be the spirit of our little society?" he asked one morning. Immediately the answer came from all.

"It must be generosity, Father."

"No self-seeking, Sophie?"

"It would be horrible, Father."

"No petty, narrow views, none of the meannesses that can grow in convents?" he asked Octavie.

"Father, how could that be if we were living in touch with God in prayer?" Octavie replied with her thoughts running to the life of union with God of a Carmelite.

"Octavie, God wants us to bring Him a heart that is not divided, and He doesn't want cowardly souls who are afraid to give Him what He wants."

"Father", Mlle. Loquet said in her decided way, "I think we understand all this. Aren't we ready to consecrate ourselves to His service?"

By November 21st, Father Varin considered that they knew enough to make a solemn consecration in the little chapel at Mlle. Duval's in front of the picture of Our Lady and the Holy Child. Mary would think of her own consecration in the Temple, and look with a mother's love at the little group of four who knelt at the altar rails before the Sacred Host held in the priest's hands and asked God to accept them too. Sophie's heart was filled with a peaceful joy and she could hardly tear herself away when Mass was ended.

"But the candle burning on the altar will remind You, dear Lord, when we are gone that we are thanking You every minute of the day", she said as she went to take her place at the breakfast table with the others.

What a day that was for happiness! Father Varin had brought Louis and another of the Fathers of the Faith to share in the graces that he felt God was bestowing. The meal seemed like the *agape* of the early Christians—why couldn't such simple holy joy last for ever? A ring came at the door. Marguerite rose to see who had so untimely broken in on them.

"A visitor for Mlle. Loquet", she said on returning.

"She doesn't want to disturb you, so she says she'll go to the chapel."

Father Varin began again to speak.

"You'll all have to be prepared to descend from the heights", he smiled as he looked at Sophie's eager face. "When a good work is begun, the devil gets busy and tries his best to wreak his spite against God——" The door was flung open violently and a lady rushed in.

"Quick! Quick!" she cried. "If you don't come at once to the chapel the house will be burnt down."

The priests sprang up and ran from the room. In the chapel the votive candle had flickered forward and caught the altar cloth. The heavy lace was burning steadily and the flames were moving towards the wooden table of the altar. In a moment or two the cloth was torn off and the fire put out.

"What did I tell you all?" Father Varin said laughingly, though there was a seriousness beneath his smile. "The devil is aroused—a moment or two later, and the altar would have been alight, and then the chapel, and then who knows? The whole house might have gone."

"And we with it", said Marguerite bluntly. "What a good thing we had a visitor. We were all so much up in the clouds that we'd never have noticed anything before we were cinders."

"And that would have been the end of the society we are dreaming of", said Octavie.

"Oh", said Sophie, "but isn't it wonderful to feel God's protection over us? It makes me not mind so much being such poor material for God to use. The love and mercy of the Sacred Heart does everything."

One day Father Varin had a new plan to propose.

"At Amiens", he said, "there is a little boarding school of some twenty children. It belongs to a good old lady who finds the work too much for her and wants her niece, Henriette Grosier, to carry on for her, but Henriette wants to enter Carmel. When I told them I could send to them some women from Paris who had decided to give themselves to God's service in His little ones, they were delighted and they are ready to hand over the school to you. There's a great friend of Henriette's too—Geneviève Deshayes, who would be quite well-to-do, but, thank God, she gives most of her money away—she wants to join you as well. She heard me preach on the text 'Go and teach', and she says she is sure that God wanted her. Now what I suggest is that Mlle. Loquet goes at once, as she is older and more experienced, and settles the business with old Mlle. Devaux, then the rest of you go later, and you can then join forces with the two young people at Amiens, with Mlle. Loquet as your superior."

Off went Mlle. Loquet to Amiens, but she found her task by no means an easy one.

"Why can't the old lady make up her mind either to give up the school or to join us?" she wondered. "So much shilly-shallying and dilly-dallying is enough to drive me mad! It's a good thing Father Varin sent me—the other two would never have enough resolution to bring matters to a head."

At length things were concluded. With many tears of regret old Mlle. Devaux left, and by November the little community were all together. Just before the anniversary of their first consecration, Father Varin came to Amiens.

"You'd better all make a retreat", he said. "It's no good making big decisions without asking God for help and light beforehand. If you want to get things clear, remember, it is 'God alone' that you must take for your motto."

On November 20th when he called to give them a final instruction, as soon as Marguerite opened the door his eyes caught a large card hung in the entry. "God alone" it read, and emphasised its message by a floral border. Shown into the parlour, he glanced at the mantelpiece; "God alone" ran the legend in red letters on a white background. He smiled and sat down at the table, pulling towards him a book of devotions that lay there. It had a marker in it. Idly he turned to it. In bold Gothic characters with elaborate flourishes he read "God alone". At that moment Geneviève Deshayes came into the room.

"Who's been writing this all over the place?" he asked her, suppressing a smile.

"Oh, it's me and Sophie", Geneviève eagerly answered him. "We've written it wherever we could find a corner. It is 'God alone', isn't it, Father? And I want Him so much that I'll burst if you don't let me make the consecration to-morrow."

Sophie came in to see the priest.

"My child," Father Varin told her, "Octavie has decided to leave us for Carmel. And now, what will you do?"

A sword seemed to go through Sophie's heart. Octavie—who had lived for so long with her, who had shared so many hopes and fears, joys and sorrows; Octavie, who had understood so well how to speak of God and to pray—and yet, "God alone, God alone".

"I mustn't change because I love any one or any place", she said at length. "Whether I like this life or not, I believe that it is God's will for me, and that's the only thing I really want. I'll stay and do all I can."

Very early the next morning, Mlle. Loquet, Geneviève, Henriette and Sophie went off with parcels under their arms to the house of a friend where there was a private chapel. They changed into the white dresses they had brought—"They look like brides", murmured old Mlle. Devaux as she saw her niece and her three companions come into the chapel. "I wish I were younger—how radiantly happy Geneviève looks!"

Mass began. Before Communion, the four moved forward to the rails to pronounce their vows. Sophie was the first.

"I thought she was the youngest", Mlle. Duclaux whispered to her friend beside her. "The oldest, Mlle. Loquet, ought to have begun."

"It's a mistake", her friend whispered back. "But never mind—it's God's arrangement."

As the months went by, Mlle. Loquet found the superior's path beset with difficulties.[1]

"It would be all right if I had some efficient helpers", she often thought. "Sister Grosier hardly knows how to turn out her room properly, Sister Deshayes goes trotting about here and trotting about there, and as for Sister Barat, she can scarcely say two words together."

Geneviève Deshayes went in for sanctity wholeheartedly.

"I suppose we are meant to do ridiculous things", she said to herself whenever her native common sense got the upper hand. "It's a test of our obedience, and so I'd better not question anything, but follow Sophie's example."

But she could not help seeing that some things in the conduct of the institution were very queer.

"Don't you notice anything wrong?" she asked Sophie one day.

"I don't see anything", Sophie answered in surprise, so

[1] In the beginnings of the Society, when Madeleine Sophie Barat and her young companions were only a pious association of women, the term *Sister* was used familiarly. Mlle. Loquet, in virtue of her age, her worldly position as authoress, and her status as Superior, seems always to have been called by this secular form of address. Madame Baudemont retained her title as a former professed Poor Clare. When the lines of the Society became clearer, the Choir nuns were called *Mother*, and the Coadjutrix Sisters, *Sister*. As novices and before final profession young Choir religious would call each other *Sister*.

Geneviève told herself ruefully, "If I were as recollected in God as Sister Sophie, I suppose I shouldn't notice anything either. Well, I'll try to be."

When the summer of 1802 came round, Father Varin, on a visit to the town, surprised the little community by saying that Sophie and Geneviève should make their final vows.

"You will come to the private chapel as you did before", he told them, "next Monday—after Whit Sunday, you should be filled with the Holy Ghost. He gives the gift of Fortitude, Sophie, don't be afraid."

The air that June morning was fresh and clear, and the birds chirped merrily under the eaves.

"Are you ready, Sister Geneviève?" asked Henriette.

"More than ready", cried the enthusiastic Geneviève. "But where's Sister Sophie?"

"I don't know—I was going to ask you. She got up a long time ago. I can't find her anywhere."

"Have you looked in the oratory?"

"Yes, but she's not there, and I've gone all through the house and she's not there. Do you think we could call?"

"We might try", said Geneviève, but there was no answer.

"It's getting late—do you think we had better go?" asked Henriette, but Geneviève suddenly cried out, "I see her—there in the garden."

Henriette joined her at the window and the two looked out into the small square of well-trodden earth, with its solitary nut tree, that was called the garden. Sophie was sitting beneath the tree.

"Sophie!" they both called. "Sister Sophie!"

Sophie sat motionless, and did not answer.

The two girls grew alarmed.

"Do you think she's ill?" Henriette asked anxiously.

"I don't know. Come along, and we'll see." Geneviève

was down the stairs and out into the garden. But when the slower Henriette caught her up, she was standing by the tree with an awed look on her face.

"Henriette," she almost whispered, "look at her face—it's—it's radiant—I've spoken to her and she doesn't answer—she just doesn't hear. I think she's having what you read about in the lives of the saints."

"An ecstasy?" Henriette prompted. "It looks like that to me. Geneviève, we can't waken her—it looks as if she was seeing what it means to be a Bride of Christ. We couldn't break into that happiness. Let's just wait."

Chapter VIII

A COG OF GOD'S MACHINERY

"IF only I had some more people to help", Mlle. Loquet frequently complained, but she was not overpleased when Father Varin sent along two postulants who had already been Poor Clares before the Revolution.

"I don't think this Madame Baudemont is meant to stay", she thought. "She has too high-and-mighty ideas—questions what I decide upon, and treats me as if I knew nothing, just because she has been a nun before. If she wants to re-establish the Poor Clares, let her go and do it. If she wants to stay, she ought to study what Father Varin wants a little more carefully."

She was not too pleased with another new arrival.

"I know she is only a farmer's daughter, and probably doesn't know she is being rude", she would tell herself. "But really, to be answered back by Sister Jugon is too much. Of course, she is very useful in the house and she does seem to put a spark of life into Sister Sophie, but she's no business to suggest to me that I'm overworking Sister Sophie and the others. Let them say so themselves if they think it."

"I don't think God means me to stay here", Sister Jugon was deciding as she fell asleep in the dormitory shared by the sisters and the masterful cook. "But perhaps He has a work for me to do. Heavens, what a draught through the door. I'm glad I'm not sleeping in the bed next to it. I'd take the middle one the cook has, if I was given a choice. No wonder she snores so well—oh, dear, how sleepy I am—and we've got to get up again at five."

It seemed to her that her head had only just touched the bolster when a loud knocking with a stick on the floor above gave the signal for rising. Shivering she dressed by the light of the one candle, and joined the others on their way to the little garret that had been converted into their chapel, leaving the cook to sleep in peace while they made their morning meditation. Geneviève led the way. When she drew level with the clock in the passage, she stopped and pointed. The hands said ten minutes past three!

"Mlle. Loquet has made a mistake again", thought Sister Jugon. "All very well for her—she's still abed. And what do we do?" she asked aloud.

"We'll go to the chapel", Sophie whispered. "We'll be able to get two more hours of prayer."

Sister Jugon did not feel as enthusiastic about it as Sophie. It would be a long time to breakfast, and then there would only be dry bread with their vegetable soup.

Breakfast over, the morning classes began. Sophie went off to the top division and was soon hard at work. "It must be hard work", Sister Jugon commented, "when you are trying to get ideas into the heads of so uninterested and undisciplined a set of children. No wonder Sister Sophie likes going to the poor school. These other young ladies want a real spanking, and I'm half inclined to tell Mlle. Loquet so."

Dinner time came round. Sister Jugon watched how Sister Sophie, Sister Geneviève and Sister Henriette, who were on duty with the children, gave them such generous servings that they left very little for themselves. By the time the last one had received her helping at Sophie's table, there came a loud outcry from the first child.

"Oh, Sister Sophie, I've finished. I want a second helping."

"I'll see if there's enough", said Sophie, spooning up

the gravy and meat that she had meant for her own share.

A shout of anger came from the little girl.

"I don't want that—there's nothing there—a lot of gravy and a horrid bit of gristle. I want a proper helping."

"Lucille", Sophie addressed the child on her left, "please run along to the kitchen and ask cook if she can spare some more meat for Clothilde."

The child obeyed. In a minute, the refectory door was flung open and the cook appeared. With arms akimbo, she glared at Sophie.

"Look here, Sister Sophie, I'll thank you not to send your messages by the children. Who do you think I am? You can come and ask yourself if you want anything else— and you'll not get it, for I've cooked all I'm going to to-day."

"Couldn't you spare a little more for Clothilde?"

"No I couldn't. And if she complains to her aunt, I'll give notice." The door was slammed to. Clothilde opened her mouth to howl, but then thought better of it. She took a large piece of roll and amused herself by crumbling it into small pieces and flicking them across the table at her companions until they had finished.

Sister Grosier cleared her throat as she sat on the chair at the end of the room, and opened a book.

"The Journey of Sophia and Eulalia to the Palace of True Happiness", she read. "Chapter Three, continued."

"Do you think that's about our Sister Sophie?" Lucille whispered to Clothilde.

"Of course not, silly", that young lady said haughtily. "My aunt wrote that book and she wouldn't be writing about a softy like that. Why, my mother says she's only a labourer's daughter. Anyhow, I don't want to listen to this story." She took up the wooden case that went round her glass and threw it on the floor. It bounced across the room, with a lovely clatter.

"Clothilde, you mustn't behave like that", Sophie remonstrated. "Go from the table until you know how to behave yourself."

"I won't", retorted Clothilde, and picked up her glass and threw it after its cover. It smashed into a thousand pieces. A small child began to cry with fright. Sophie was on her knees picking up the bits.

"Go out of the room at once", she ordered. Clothilde gripped the table with both hands and began wailing.

"I won't go out; I won't, I tell you. You're being cruel to me. Oh, oh, oh!" She kept a weather eye on the door, and when it opened and Mlle. Loquet appeared, she broke into uncontrolled sobs.

"What is it, darling?" Mlle. Loquet asked with her arms round Clothilde's shaking shoulders. "Have you been upsetting her again, Sister Sophie?"

"Oh, don't scold her, Auntie." Clothilde stopped crying for a moment. "I'll forgive her."

"But I can't have you in this state, dearie. Sister Sophie, haven't you more sense? Why, the child is in such a state that she'll be unfit for the afternoon classes."

"I think I'd feel better in the open air", Clothilde murmured. "Don't you think all the division could go out? We'd take Sister Sophie with us—and you'll see that we forgive."

"That's quite a good idea. Sister Sophie, you may take your class, but Sister Jugon can go with you to see that there is no repetition of this unkind treatment. Sister Deshayes, you had better take your class too."

At one-thirty, the two crocodiles were waiting at the door with the Sisters for Mlle. Loquet's blessing on their departure.

"What awful frights we look", thought Sister Jugon, surveying the curious dress the Sisters were wearing. "How could Mlle. Loquet have thought out a costume quite so ridiculous—especially putting this silly little round bonnet on top of it all. Doesn't she know it's only the poorest people in Amiens that wear them? And there's the well-known Geneviève Deshayes going about in it, and pretending not to see the sniggers of her old friends when she meets them in the street."

Mlle. Loquet came out. Clothilde sprang to the attack.

"Auntie", she said innocently, "may we go to the Hotoie?"

"Oh, no", said Sister Deshayes. "That's a very fashionable promenade."

"Well, we are very fashionable", said Clothilde smirking and taking a few mincing steps. There was a titter. Mlle. Loquet turned on the children.

"How dare you laugh like that in my presence?" she scolded, and the surprised children were silent.

"Well, Auntie?" Clothilde knew how far she could go.

"Your band may go. Those with Sister Deshayes will not." She went back to her room.

As soon as the orderly file reached the promenade, Clothilde whispered, "Come along, let's walk faster, and make Sister Sophie run."

No sooner thought than done. The children quickened their pace, but Sister Sophie and Sister Jugon could keep up.

"Run", cried Clothilde, "and scatter."

And poor Sophie was left in the middle of a well-dressed crowd with all her charges vanished.

"Cheer up", Sister Jugon said, "I'll shout for you—my voice carries better than yours in the open air."

There was no doubt about it. The amused passers-by watched the two curiously-dressed young women as the sturdy taller one, by dint of shouting and running, gathered the scattered flock together like a good sheep-dog.

"We're dreadfully sorry, Sister Sophie", three of them

said on the way back. "The others are too, only they're not brave enough to say so—we do love you, but it's such fun when Clothilde plays about."

That night when the children were safe in their dormitory, Sophie, Geneviève and Henriette made their way to the kitchen vacated by the cook who had herself retired to bed. Gathered round the candle with their heads close together, they were laughing and talking while their fingers were busy mending the stockings of the little girls. Sister Jugon came into the room with pen, ink and paper. Sophie looked up and asked:

"Are you going to write? You'll need the candle. We can manage by the firelight."

"No, thank you", Sister Jugon said thoughtfully. "My letter will not take long, and your talk won't interrupt me. What are you laughing about?"

"Why", answered Geneviève, "here was Sophie wishing to go to the missions in Canada, and Henriette talking of converting hundreds of heathens, and when they ask me what I want to do, all I can say is that I don't seem to have even enough zeal for France itself—I said I felt as if I had a candle extinguisher on me."

"I wonder what you'd feel like if the extinguisher was removed", said Sister Jugon and began writing.

> "Dear Father Varin,
>   As I do not think I have a vocation to stay in your society, I think I have the right to tell you some of the things that go on in the house. . . ."

"It's time we went up to bed", Sophie said some time later. "That's a very long letter of yours, Sister."

"It's finished now", Adèle Jugon replied and went up to the dormitory and slept the sleep of the just.

A few days later she left Amiens.

The next time Father Varin came, Geneviève was downcast.

"It's such a sad thing, Father, when someone leaves us—it must hurt Our Lord when they turn away from Him."

"You can't say that, my child, of anyone with certainty. They answer a call, and do what they think right. Perhaps it is only one thing that God wants from them. Adèle Jugon came, and now she has gone. But I think she has done the one thing that God wanted."

Chapter IX

SENTENCED FOR LIFE

A DELE JUGON's letter alarmed Father Varin. He knew that she was a level-headed and generous girl who was not likely to exaggerate a bad situation. He had suspected for some time past that Mlle. Loquet was not a person so meek and humble of heart that she could hold the highest position in the house and yet think herself the lowest of all. But he himself was busy with missions up and down France, and could not investigate the true state of affairs. Instead he sent the capable Madame Naudet from the school that the Archduchess Marie-Anne had opened in Rome. It did not take long for her to size up the trouble.

"Your little society is in great danger", she told the Sisters when Mlle. Loquet was not present. "If things go on as they are, you are heading for complete ruin."

They listened to her in awed silence. They each knew that matters were not as they should be, but this was the first time it had been said aloud. Ruin! The end of all their hopes for the glory of the Sacred Heart and the salvation of souls. They were appalled.

"But can't we do something?" Geneviève burst out.

"Isn't there someone who can help us?" Henriette questioned.

Sophie was silent, thinking. When Herod sought the life of the Child Jesus, Mary kept Him safe in her arms. Couldn't she hold them safely, too?

As though to answer her thoughts, Madame Naudet went on.

"Prayer alone can help. Ten days from now is the Feast of the Assumption. We'll make a novena to the Queen of Heaven, and ask her for light and aid."

"Good", cried Geneviève. "Can we do some penances— pretty stiff ones—and have permission to stay up later at night to get some extra prayer?"

"I think it would be a good thing for one of us to be in retreat each day", Sophie suggested. "The others could share her work and she could be asking Our Lady at every possible minute of the day."

If Geneviève expected a sudden miracle on the Feast of the Assumption, she was disappointed. But Father Varin was not. More and more clearly did the conduct of Mlle. Loquet show her unsuitability for the work de Tournély had dreamed of. When he came to Amiens in November, he spoke very seriously to the Superior.

"But I don't know how they will possibly get on without me", Mlle. Loquet affirmed, with a shake of her head that foretold disaster to the whole scheme when she was not there to guide it. "They are still so incapable—I have to tell them every little thing to do. Still, as you say my services will be of greater use to God back in Paris, I suppose I had better go. They have been crying out for me there to reopen my work-room for poor girls. Perhaps, too, I shall then have proper leisure to write some more books—people appreciate the good that can be done by composing books —there", she added with her head held high.

Although she had made them suffer, it was with heavy hearts that the rest of the little band saw her go in the first week of December. Madame Naudet would have to go to her own convent. Who could help them to recover from the blow of their desertion, and regain the simple light-hearted courage that had been theirs in the beginning?

On the twenty-first of December, they sat on the edge of their chairs in the best parlour waiting for the arrival of Father Varin. He would be able to settle the hard question of who should be superior.

"I wonder which of us it is to be", thought Henriette, glancing round their circle surreptitiously. "Madame Baudemont has had experience of convent life but—she frightens me somehow."

"Thank God it won't be me", thought Geneviève. "I'll have to learn a good deal more patience before anyone bothers their head about giving me a post of responsibility —and get a good deal more wisdom, too—oh heavens, yes, and general holiness—thank God the burden won't be mine."

"They're all so young", Madame Baudemont pondered, as she looked at the downcast heads of the others, settling herself in her chair. "I can't quite see any of them having the *savoir-faire*—a superior doesn't only have to deal with her community. There are parents of children, priests, bishops, even the civil authorities—you need someone who has reached the maturity of a certain age. Mlle. Loquet had at least that advantage. I must be the only one left now who has years on her side."

"What a pity Sister Sophie has such poor health," Madame Naudet was commenting to herself. "And if only she would learn to come out of herself more!"

"I must do everything I can to help her", Sophie told herself. "It must be dreadful to be a superior. To have the care and happiness of every one in your hands—to know God holds you responsible for helping them—I must try to be a good daughter to her—I'll pray for her—and try not to cause her anxiety—please God I'll always be obedient to her—it must be dreadful to have to give orders to other people—and to have to take the first place—and——"

She stopped thinking of what she would do as Father Varin walked into the room. He had another priest with him and looked very solemn.

"We have come, my dear Sisters", he said, "to examine you on Christian doctrine."

Madame Baudemont sat up in surprise. What about the choice of superior which they had been led to understand by Madame Naudet was to be settled to-day? Father Varin ignored her murmur of impatience.

"Where is Sister Sophie?" he asked, and as she stood up, "Sister", he continued, "as you are the youngest, it's right that I should put the simplest questions to you. Well, now, why has God created you and put you in this world?"

"To know Him", she replied, as simply as when she stood on the bench in St. Thibault's, "to love Him and to serve Him."

"What do you mean by serving God?" Father Varin was looking at her very seriously.

"It's doing His Will", she answered again.

"Good." Father Varin's voice rang out with authority. "Then the Will of God is that you should be Superior."

Sophie, thunderstruck, fell on her knees. She didn't see the smiles of delight that were on her companions' faces.

"Oh, Father", she sobbed, with the tears streaming down her cheeks, "I—I—I'm just a nothing—I couldn't be superior—please, please, have mercy on me——"

Father Varin looked down on her as she knelt clasping her hands in front of him. He saw what it meant now to her, he guessed what it would mean to her in the future. He glanced up and caught a slight look of impatience on Madame Baudemont's face. He saw anxiety as to what his decision would be on Geneviève's. He remembered again

E

de Tournély's words as he lay dying, "My dearest friend, I have entrusted everything to you." Father Varin knew this time that he was not mistaken. Here was the foundation stone, small enough, humble enough, for God to build on. Though he was cut to the heart to see Sophie's distress, he remained inflexible.

"You will do God's Will, *Mother* Barat", he said. Then as Geneviève clapped her hands for very joy, he said with a twinkle, "I'll leave her to you now, my dear Sisters."

"Oh, how pleased I am", cried Henriette springing up. But Sophie had mastered her tears. She motioned to them to stay where they were.

"I am so sorry for you", she said, "to have me for your mother——" and before they could stop her, she had kissed the feet of all her daughters.

There were plenty of people ready to criticise the choice of a girl of twenty-three for Superior, but there were plenty who saw a change coming about in the conduct of the school that made them ready to defend the new order of things.

"It's so happy at school now", Lucille told her mother. "Everyone seems to go about smiling—I mean the Sisters as well as us—and you know, since Clothilde has gone, we don't want to be so naughty. I think that's partly because the lessons are so interesting—we love Mother Barat's—especially when she talks to us about God. Oh, and then, they keep on getting more teachers—why, would you believe it, one came riding down the street the other day on a horse—it was a bit of a scraggy one, but then it had come over two hundred miles—asking to join their society—and ever so many of them can tell you all sorts of thrilling things about the way they hid priests or were put in prison during the Revolution. They seem to have had such exciting times", Lucille said wistfully. "It's no wonder they're holy."

"Are they?" asked her mother.

"Well, Mother Barat says she's not, but we think differently. They get cross if we say so. The other day Caroline crept up behind Mother Grosier and kissed the hem of her dress. 'What on earth are you up to?' Mother Grosier asked. 'Please—you went to Holy Communion this morning', Caroline answered. So I think we are right in thinking they're holy", Lucille concluded triumphantly.

"In that case, Lucille", her mother remarked, "you can be holy without all the exciting times and I shall expect to see your halo on a head that has escaped the guillotine. Now, what about getting on with your home-work?"

"Oh, Mother", Lucille began, "can't I just finish this story?" Then she caught her mother's eye. "Yes, Mother, I'll begin straight away."

"At least they are showing her the value of duty", thought her mother. "I like that little Superior, too. She's so ready to listen to your troubles. I expect she's the same with her daughters. She cheers you up somehow. Well, I hope they'll keep her a long time as Superior."

Chapter X

THE ENDS OF THE EARTH

A SOLITARY light was burning in the inn-yard of the Coq d'Or at Lyons. The breath of the horses smoked in the sharp December air as they stamped and jingled their harness.

"Steady, there", said the stable boy as he fastened a strap, and then, to the coachman standing beating his arms against his chest, "What time are you off, Jules?"

"Half-past five. I'm only waiting for the three ladies—they would go off to Mass, though I said they'd be better getting their beauty-sleep in a warm bed. The gentleman's inside."

"Got many passengers?"

"No, most people know better than to travel to Grenoble at this time of year—there's only the three ladies—I can't quite place them—they're not a bit alike, and yet I've heard them call each other 'Sister', and bless me if they didn't say 'Mother' to the very youngest looking one of the lot—the little, quick, good-looking one. It fair beats me."

"Who's the gent, Jules?" the stable boy asked straightening his back as he finished his job.

"Oh, I know him. He's a writer of Grenoble—he's always going round pottering about History—very interested in the past, you know. He means to write a treatise on saints—relics of a bygone mentality, he calls them—says they'd be anachronisms to-day when we've got liberty, fraternity and equality. Ah, here come the ladies—pleasant, aren't they?"

As the little party of nuns entered the yard, the inn-keeper's wife appeared at the door, driving before her a small ragged boy who ducked skilfully to avoid her blows.

"I'll give you what for!" she shouted at him. "You just let me catch you again trying to sneak food. Be off with you."

The boy backed out of reach and put out his tongue. Turning quickly he ran into the sturdy arms of Sister Marguerite.

"That's not the way to behave", she said, holding him firmly. "What were you trying to take food for?"

"I was hungry", the boy snivelled.

"But don't you know it's wrong to steal?" Sister Marguerite asked him.

"Nobody never told me so", said the boy. "Why is it?"

"It's breaking one of the Ten Commandments", she told him.

"What are they?" he asked, rubbing his ragged sleeve across his dirty face, but Sophie interrupted the catechism.

"Sister Debrosse, where's my black bag? There's a ginger-bread cake there he could have." She brought it out and handed it to the boy. He seized it and devoured it ravenously. Marguerite looked on with disapproval.

"But, Mother," she said, "that was for your dinner."

"He needs it more. Look how hungry he is for it—what a pity we can't feed his soul so easily—it'll be a life work to give food to all these poor children who have been deprived of their knowledge of God."

"Take your places, ladies", the coachman called, and they climbed into the coach. The gentleman had already ensconced himself in the far corner and was enveloped in rugs. The stable boy opened the door again, and looked in. Glancing at their shawls and ungloved hands, he said, "You're going to be mighty cold, ladies. Put your feet in this." So saying, he thrust inside a large armful of straw, and shut the door, grinning with pleasure to see their gratitude.

In a few minutes the coach was out of the yard and travelling along the main road to Grenoble in the dark December morning. It did not take long for their travelling companion to settle down in his corner and snooze happily. They finished their morning meditation, and then the mind of each one went ahead of the stage coach to their goal. Sister Marguerite's thoughts jingled in her head with the shaking of the harness, "I'm going to a monastery —a monastery—a monastery—I've never seen a proper one—a proper one—a proper one—I guess there will be grilles and things—and little cells—and corridors—I'm going to a monastery—a monastery——"

Sister Debrosse's moods jolted up and down with the bumping of the coach.

"How wonderful to be journeying right across France to be one of the first to open the second house of our Society— but, heavens, only a few weeks ago I was only a novice— what an honour—but what a responsibility—fancy going to a real convent—but it's very poor—what an adventure— but oh, I do miss the others at Amiens—it's lovely being with Mother Barat—but what's this new person at Grenoble going to be like?—they say she's quite old— thirty-five at least——"

The day was beginning to lighten but, except when they passed through villages, there was little to be seen as yet save a white world of mist and hoarfrost. Sophie was listening to the measured beat of the horses' feet and the forward rolling of the wheels.

"On and on", she thought, "not seeing clearly where we are going—but trusting to the driver—on and on—we might really be going to the ends of the earth—that was what Father Varin said. 'At Grenoble you will find some-one waiting to help you. If she were alone at the ends of

the earth, you ought to go in search of her.' At the ends
of the earth—at the ends of the earth. How I wish I could
go to the ends of the earth and tell all people of the love of
God. But I suppose I am tied here. When first we thought
of our Society at Mlle. Duval's, when the priest from
Madagascar told me of the heathens who were still waiting
for the Gospel, I wanted to go to the very ends of the
earth. But I was told I must remain in France—You
haven't forgotten, dear Lord, that I asked You then for a
companion who one day could do that work instead of me
and better than me—at the ends of the earth—at the ends
of the earth."

The coachman pulled up.

"There's a steepish bit of hill here", he said, "and the
ground's slippery. It'd be a help to the horses if the
passengers would get out and walk to the top."

Grumblingly the gentleman unrolled himself from his
cocoon of rugs. Sophie and her two companions climbed
out and set off up the hill.

"It's a good thing to feel your feet again", Marguerite
remarked. "Mine were getting like lumps of ice."

At the top of the rise, they stood still and caught their
breath. Before them fields and low hills were levelled out in
a white mist that covered their details like a swirling sea,
from which, high, majestic, their snow-crowned peaks
golden in the rays of the sun, rose the mountains, clear-cut
against a dazzling blue sky.

"He stood and measured the earth, and the everlasting
mountains were scattered and the perpetual hills did bow",
cried Sister Debrosse. "Oh Mother, it looks as if we were
coming to the uttermost parts of the earth."

"I will lift up my eyes to the hills", Marguerite began.

"From whence cometh my help", Sophie finished and
was silent.

Back in the coach, the gentleman was inclined to chat.

"Very interesting country we're passing through, ladies. Now, over there up that branch of the road, among the forests you can just see, there is the Grande Chartreuse—curiously there were actually monks living there before the Revolution, in precisely the same way as when St. Bruno settled there six hundred years ago. You wouldn't think medieval ideas could have lasted so long."

Sister Marguerite listened to him with open mouth. What was he talking about?

"There's another interesting monastery on the hill outside Grenoble", he went on. "Ste. Marie d'en Haut. Not so old, of course. Founded in 1604 for the Visitation Nuns. Jane Frances de Chantal lived there at one time. Bishop Francis of Sales helped her—they were good people with the mistaken idea that they could get people to live like early and medieval Christians. Couldn't see that you must move with the times. And the curious thing is that they nearly succeeded. It needed the Revolution—and you may remember that that began at the castle of Vizille, just near Grenoble—to convince people that the days of saints were over. Now, you, I dare swear", he said, fixing Sister Debrosse with a bland smile, "have never seen a saint".

"I have," Sister Marguerite stated stoutly, "with my very own eyes."

"Oh, Marguerite", Sophie remonstrated softly, "Father Varin isn't a canonised saint."

"I wasn't thinking of him", Marguerite said firmly and shut her mouth tight, pulled out her rosary under her shawl, and began saying it for the enlightenment of the enlightened gentleman who was saying so many strange things.

"I'll explain what I mean", he continued. "There were nuns at Ste. Marie's right up to the eve of the Revolution. With the Terror, they dispersed. A few of them came back after, egged on by Mlle. Duchesne who had been a novice there, but they couldn't stay. They realised that convents belonged to the days that had passed. The freedom of man's mind has done away with them. You don't need them in 1804."

It was Sister Debrosse's turn to look astonished.

"But it is to Ste. Marie that we are going", she said.

"Really?" The gentleman looked at them with mild interest. "Oh, yes, I had heard a rumour about Mlle. Duchesne's running a school, or something of the sort, for ragged children—I suppose you will be helping her. She has energy for six, has Mlle. Philippine—I know her father, and her father's father was one of the great figures of my boyhood. I'd have run a mile rather than meet him—they all have strong characters, the Duchesnes. I think Mlle. Philippine has more than a touch of the Duchesne spirit. I understand her family has strongly disapproved of her goings-on. They considered it a sheer waste of money to buy the old monastery, and as for living there alone, and sweeping and cleaning the place herself, well, if she were not the daughter of an old acquaintance of mine, Madame, I should say she was a curious medieval survival also."

It was late afternoon when they entered Grenoble. The coach pulled up in the public place and Sophie and her companions got out.

"Ste. Marie d'en Haut is up the hill there", the gentleman told them kindly, but he did not offer to show them the way because he had just thought of a new chapter for his book, pointing out the necessity of establishing schools to help to bring about an age of enlightenment, and he was afraid that if he did not get his ideas on paper quickly he would forget the neat turns of expression that were now in his head. Up the hill they trudged, leaving the town and its clustered roofs behind them, and as the road wound higher, the semi-circle of mountains rose to meet them across the valley of the Isère. Swift and cold and dark the waters of the river ran, swollen with the winter snows, but the mountains spread their untrodden whiteness before their eyes, peak beyond peak.

"You couldn't be little or narrow, looking at this view", sighed Sister Debrosse—"it makes you think the whole world is lying stretched before you."

"Ah", said Sophie, "if we are to win or to train souls, our own must be great and wide, wide as the ocean. Father Varin says St. Francis Xavier undertook to convert the world because his soul was greater than the world."

Sister Marguerite, who was stepping out in front, stopped.

"I think we must be here", she said, pointing to a door that lay at the end of a little cobbled alley. They turned to take one last look at the mountains. In the west the red December sun had just sunk, and now the scarps of the mountains stood out grey and formidable like a great fortress, rugged and strong.

"I think they were much more lovely when the sun was playing on them", Sister Debrosse remarked. "It softened them, somehow. They still looked strong, but they were more attractive."

Marguerite, knocking on the door, thought the grey, rugged, stone buildings that lay in front of them were by no means attractive either. A bell tinkled in a little belfry. The door was opened by an old woman with a shawl round her head.

"Go along the corridor there", she mumbled. "Come in quick and shut the door—it's cold—and some of the windows are out."

"What a queer low corridor", Sister Debrosse thought, as they began walking along the flagged passage.

"Good gracious, if the whole place is as damp as this, Mother Barat will be dead in a week", Sister Marguerite muttered to herself. Sophie was watching the end of the corridor. A tall strong-faced woman had appeared. When she caught sight of the small frail form advancing towards her, she hastened her step. Like a whirlwind she was upon them, and before Sophie could stop her, Mlle. Duchesne was down on her knees and kissing her feet. With a look of unrestrained joy, she lifted her head and cried:

"At last I see upon the mountains the feet of those who come to give us tidings of peace and true good! God be praised that He has let me prepare this place for Him." Then before Sophie had recovered from her surprise, Mlle. Duchesne was up and calling to her companions.

"We can't express our happiness", she explained as her four friends gathered round their new mother.

"It's the day we've all been longing for", they said.

"And I too", said their new mother and took them all to her heart.

Chapter XI

SUN ON THE MOUNTAIN

Y EARS afterwards, when Philippine Duchesne was old and lonely in a far-off land, her thoughts would turn back to those first days when Mother Barat came to show her the burning love of the Sacred Heart, and her courage would be once more warmed into life.

That first Christmas Eve she had suddenly realised that the house to which she had invited her new Superior was cold and bleak. She had not minded for herself, she was strong enough to bear any hardships, and she had not minded it for her companions, until she had discovered that Mother Barat was going round and trying to relieve the excessive suffering of their privations.

"I am so sorry that this is so poor a place to welcome you", she said sadly. Mother Barat smiled merrily.

"Sorry? Why should you be? I am glad with all my heart that we can live here like the Holy Family. It's like being in Bethlehem. I would not change it for anything— He was not in the inn, remember."

When the bell summoned them for the midnight office, Philippine Duchesne noted with distress that the snow had piled itself up in the corridor through the open doorway where the door had long ago fallen from its hinges. But outside the moon rode high in a clear sky, and the hillside sparkled and the trees bore their dazzling white foliage with quiet pride. There was a hush over everything—the world seemed to be waiting in expectation.

"It is like Bethlehem", she thought. "We're waiting for

Our Lord to be born anew. I wouldn't be anywhere else either."

Inside the chapel, the snow had sifted in through the broken windows, but in the sanctuary there was a blaze of candles, and the linen altar cloth was spotless.

"We've done what we could, as Mother Barat asked us, to welcome the King who is to come, but she says that that is only an outside welcome", thought Philippine. "What about our hearts?"

The priest began the Mass. At the Consecration, God's Almighty Word leaped down from Heaven and they worshipped the Child, lying helpless and bound as in the crib at Bethlehem.

"Give me Your humility, Your gentleness, Your love of poverty, O God, You who have made Yourself nothing for my sake", Sophie prayed.

"O Divine Son of the Father, obedient to His Will, teach me to be obedient", Philippine asked Him.

"Give me the faith of the shepherds to see You in all the little things I shall be asked to do", Sister Debrosse prayed. "And keep me silent like You when my self-love is hurt."

"O dear little Jesus", Sister Marguerite was so happy that she did not want to talk much, "I'm only like the old ox or the ass, but their breath kept You warm. Just come into my heart and I'll do my best to keep out the cold."

At recreations Mother Barat brought along a little statue of the Holy Child and gave Him a place of honour.

"Let us come often to the Crib", she urged them all. "How can we fear this God who is a Child? Oh, no, we can only love Him."

"He is so small", mused Sister Rivet, looking at the tiny statue.

"And yet everything was made by Him—look out of the window and see the great mountains and the filigree snow-flakes", Mother Barat reminded her.

"What a lot of things He gives us", said Sister Marguerite, with her eye on a robin who was pecking up crumbs she had spread on the sill.

"Very well", Mother Barat suggested to them, "give Him something in return—just any stupid little thing that is keeping you back from Him—a tiny fault, a bit of self-love, some silly conceit—but, don't make bargains with Our Lord. Give everything and you will receive everything. Dear Lord, what is our little everything, when you put it up against the great Everything—the Heart of Jesus?"

Sister Rivet was thoughtful. "Mother", she said slowly, "I see now why we don't need grilles to shut us off from the world inside our convent—it is the love of Our Lord that is our enclosure."

"And I think I see why you don't want us to wear rough clothes like the Poor Clares, or rags like the Fathers of the desert", Sister Giraud remarked.

"Why?" asked Philippine Duchesne.

"It might frighten people away", said Emily Giraud. "And we are only here to invite people in out of the snow to warm themselves at Our Lord's Sacred Heart."

But Philippine's heroic soul longed to follow the austerities of the Fathers of the desert, even if she could not emulate their rags.

"Philippine", Mother Barat said to her one day, "you had better not put bitter herbs on all your food." Philippine's face fell.

"Of course I will do as you say, Mother."

"And, Philippine, the father who preached to you all yesterday asked you to bring to my door anything which you set any store on—I have had nothing, and the father is complaining.

Again Philippine looked embarrassed.

"But, Mother", she answered quickly, "I couldn't put

the house and everybody in it at your door, and those are the only things I set any store on."

Obedience, she was beginning to learn, was everything. But all the same she so wanted to suffer for the spread of God's Kingdom that when a decent interval had elapsed, she asked again if she could mix bitter herbs with her food.

"Very well", replied Mother Barat, "on condition that I don't notice it." The joy that had leaped up at her first words died as quickly. "I always sit next to her", Philippine thought. "How can I do it without her seeing? I'll try, anyhow. Perhaps if I cut them up small she won't notice."

When dinner came, for the first time Philippine watched Mother Barat carefully.

"Good gracious!" she exclaimed with inward delight. "She doesn't notice anything once she's said Grace—her thoughts are with God the whole time—I can just do what I want—but I shall have to be careful not to boast of it."

However, months later when Mother Barat was on the point of leaving, she could not resist putting a large label on her place in the refectory.

"Wake not my Beloved until she please."

And Mother Barat joined heartily in the laugh against herself.

"I am glad when you are merry", she said. "Father Varin is always saying, 'Be gay! The joy of the bride gives honour to the Bridegroom.'"

"You see things in their right proportions if you can laugh", Sister Rivet remarked.

"Yes", added Sister Giraud, "a saint that is sorry for herself is a sorry saint."

But one of Philippine's best joys was to find that Mother Barat shared in her great desire to be a missionary, and to spread through the whole world the knowledge of God's

love. The problem that had vexed her soul when she was a
novice of the Visitation, of leading a life of prayer when
her heart burned to go forth to foreign lands like St. Francis
Xavier, seemed to be resolved. She was still on her mountain in France, but Mother Barat, journeying up and down
the land to make new foundations, was preparing the way.
Soon, surely, the day would come when she would send a
party out from France, from the Old World to the New,
to carry the message of the Sacred Heart to those who still
sat in darkness.

In January, 1806, Sophie was called to Amiens, and
elected Superior-General of the three houses of the Society
that now existed. Father Varin was there, with Father
Roger of the Fathers of the Faith, and they thought it right
to have for a witness the chaplain of the house, M. l'Abbé
de Saint-Estève—and a little cloud, the size of a man's
hand, appeared over the horizon.

Sophie consoled herself for this fresh burden put upon
what she considered her unworthiness by reading the
letters that Philippine was writing to her, beseeching her to
send her abroad.

"How good God is to give us someone to go to the missions with courage and a love of the Cross", Sophie
thought, "how kind to satisfy my desires in her—how
consoling it will be to go to speak of Our Lord to hearts that
are fresh and have not abused His graces—but we cannot
abandon the souls here in Europe who give us more trouble
and less consolation. To save a soul—what a sublime
vocation!" She picked up again the pages covered with
Philippine's fine writing, and smiled as she read her thanks
for being allowed to pass the whole of Maundy Thursday
night in the chapel. "Philippine gathered up the Precious
Blood where It had been shed in the Garden of the Agony,
in the Pretorium, and on Calvary, and carried It to the

New World", Sophie mused, thinking of the feathered chieftains on the prairies and in the forests of the Rockies hastening to bow before It, but there rose up too before her eyes the palm-fringed islands of the Pacific stretching beyond the Americas, the closed islands of Japan, and the yellow peoples of China looked at her with their almond eyes. She saw the teeming millions of India moving to worship at the summons of the temple-bell or the call of the muezzin, the age-old peoples of Egypt, the ebony men in the dark unknown forests of Africa; then her thoughts swept northward to a Europe that was turning away from its ancient inheritance, and northward further still where the Seamless Robe had already been rent by schism, while everywhere the Chosen People lived scattered in proof of man's rejection of his Saviour. And here was Philippine Duchesne overflowing with eager petition to be sent— "When you say to me, 'Behold I send you', I shall lose no time in saying, 'I go'," ran the letter, but Sophie shook her head. Better than her daughter, she knew the difficulties that lay in the way.

"The Spring sun is melting the snows and the Isère is getting very full and swift", Mother Debrosse remarked one day at recreation.

"Do you know", Sister Marguerite said with eyes wide with wonder, "that the greater part of the river comes from a glacier miles and miles away—Mother Rivet told me it takes hundreds of years for the ice to creep down the mountain to the place where it melts—just think of the time some of the drops of water in the river have taken to get to Grenoble——"

"And what a time they have still to wait before they get to the sea", laughed Mother Rivet.

Philippine Duchesne kept silent. She was thinking of the words of Mother Barat, "You are in too great a hurry.

God's work is done in the shade and slowly. The Psalmist says, 'A thousand years are in Thy sight as yesterday'." She did not want to wait, but if that was God's way, she would try to be content. The bell for the end of recreation sounded. She picked up a Grammar book and went up to the class of little girls that awaited her.

"Mother", coaxed the children when she appeared, "if we're good, will you tell us all about the Jesuit martyrs in Canada?"

"Perhaps", said Philippine. "If you can wait patiently till the end of the lesson."

Chapter XII

MAN PROPOSES...

I<small>N</small> 1799 the Little Corporal was First Consul. By 1804 strong rule at home and successful armies abroad made it possible for him to place on his own head the Imperial Crown while the age-long saints in their niches in Notre Dame looked down with surprise at this self-appointed successor of Charlemagne. Austerlitz, Jena—and Nelson dead—now Europe lay before him, and beyond, the riches of India and the East and the great territories of the Tsar, awaiting conquest; then west across the Atlantic New France invited him and the vast resources of the Americas—world empire and a power greater than Alexander's, wider than Charlemagne's. It was a pity that an old Pope should baulk his plans, should not be ready to fall in with his desires for a useful combination of State and Church. "A State without religion", said Napoleon, "is like a ship without a compass; there is no good morality without religion", and from his very camp he signed the decree permitting Mother Barat to open her schools. But since the Fathers of the Faith were like Jesuits, ready to support the Holy Father through thick and thin, they must be disbanded, and he gave the order for their dispersal in 1807. With Rome and the Papal States in his grasp, it was a very little thing that his prisoner Pius VII should give his blessing to a small number of schoolgirls and their mistresses from a poor convent on the mountain-side at Grenoble, or that they should promise to pray for the needs of the Church and ask the protection of the Sacred

Heart for the Ship of Peter. Greater things than that were filling his mind and the campaign that should take him triumphantly into Moscow was shaping itself.

Mother Barat was campaigning too. The years were filled with journeyings up and down France, and the opening of other houses. There were many who were asking to become religious, devoted to the glory of the Sacred Heart, even though the times were too dangerous to take that Name openly as yet. From all parts they came, aristocrats and peasants, well-known and of no repute, educated and illiterate, old and young, women on whom God seemed to have lavished gifts of rare intelligence, and simple souls whose treasure was a heart that loved. At Poitiers she gathered them together and from her own overflowing love taught them how to serve the Master who had kept back nothing in His gift to them, showing them His Heart pierced by the ingratitude of men, and reminding them that the wounds that cut most deeply were those that came from the half-heartedness and coldness of those consecrated to Him in religious orders. Here in the old abbey that had become their home the novices caught from their Mother General the flaming zeal and the deep humility that would send them out to conquer the world for the Sacred Heart, trusting only in the power of God. Mother Barat thanked God daily that she was allowed to see so many valiant soldiers arming with the sword of the Spirit. Poitiers was a place of refuge from the sorrows that she had to face in other places.

At Ste. Marie d'en Haut, they noticed that when Amiens was mentioned Mother Barat had little to say—the more deep-seeing were aware of a sadness that clouded her face when her travels took her to or from the very cradle of the Order, but no word did she say as to what was troubling her. During one of her absences, a long letter arrived from

Amiens, from Mother Baudemont, now Superior there, and M. de Saint-Estève.

"What kind of a man is this Abbé de Saint-Estève?" Mother Duchesne asked Mother Deshayes, now at Grenoble.

Geneviève paused before answering, her mind going back to the days before she and Henriette left to take up their work in the new houses. "I don't want to be uncharitable", she said at last, "and I am afraid I am still feeling sore about the way in which he and Mother Baudemont arranged things at Amiens, as though there was no Mother General to consult. I think he is a literary man, with a brilliant imagination." She stopped.

"Well?" asked Philippine.

"But he's always on the climb", added Mother Deshayes, weighing her words. "It was he who got the Bishop to send Julie Billiart away from the Sisters of Notre Dame, because he wanted to direct them and did not see the point of having a Mother General for them, and it was he who sent a party of our nuns from Amiens to open a house at Ghent, and he allows it to be said openly that he is our founder. God forgive me if I am wronging him when I say he is an ambitious man and no more understands the spirit of Our Lord, meek and humble of Heart, than the Emperor himself."

"I can see he has an imagination", Mother Duchesne said ruefully, opening out the sheets she held in her hands. "These rules and constitutions he has sent for our acceptance—well, they are a literary compilation of some skill! But I don't see anything of the Rule of St. Ignatius in them, and Father de Tournély meant us to add to the glory of the Jesuit Saint by being enrolled among his children."

"St. Basil's Rule seems to be the foundation", Mother Deshayes reflected, "and it looks as if he has put in some of the Ursuline Rules that his sister remembers, and then added a dash of Poor Clare from Mother Baudemont and goodness knows what hotchpotch of his own ideas. This is not what I became a nun of the Sacred Heart for."

"He doesn't even want us to have that name", remarked Philippine with some warmth. "Apostolines is his invention for us—I might wear the new habit he's concocted with Mother Baudemont, that doesn't really matter—but I won't take this new name—our name is the very reason of our existence. Why doesn't Mother Barat make short shrift of all this? Why doesn't she do something?"

"I expect Mother Barat has more wisdom than you and I", said Geneviève, "and can wait in case hasty action divides us all. And as for doing anything, well, I think I see now why she has gone from house to house teaching us more of the spirit of Our Lord and warming us with the fire of His Love. And now she is with Father Varin at his sister's château near Besançon—it's an ill wind that blows nobody any good. If he were not forbidden to preach, he would never have the leisure to write down with her the Rules and Constitutions that we have been living since the first days of the Society."

At the château of Chevroz in the autumn of 1813, Ferdinand Jeantier found life full of interest. At twelve, it was a great privilege to be allowed to serve Mass each morning for a priest who was suffering because he wanted to be a Jesuit—and that was what Ferdinand had set his own heart upon. And it was intriguing to wonder what the man who was so full of fun could be doing as he walked up and down the garden, pencil and notebook in hand, talking so seriously to Madame Barat for hours on end.

And then there was Madame Barat who everybody was saying was a saint. "It isn't everyone who lives with a saint," thought Ferdinand, and studied her surreptitiously to see what exactly saints did. But she was just like other people to talk to, except that she never lost her temper with him and would help him with his lessons if he wanted, and was very good at making jokes, and every bit as fond of the poor soldiers of the Grand Army making their way back from the disastrous retreat from Moscow.

"Perhaps it's her prayer that makes her a saint", he decided one evening. "She spends hours and hours before the Blessed Sacrament. Why, the other night she actually forgot that it was supper time, and I had to go with a lantern to the church to look for her. It was pretty hard to find her among the benches, hidden away like a mouse and much quieter—and I had to call her several times before she heard me. I expect that's what they mean when they say someone is lost in God—only she looked much more as though she was found in God. Hullo, there's a soldier at the door begging."

He ran downstairs and, meeting Sophie on the way, cried out, "Madame Barat, come with me—there's a soldier in the kitchen—perhaps he'll be able to tell us about the war."

The man was a pitiful sight, but he pulled himself to a semblance of attention when they greeted him, and asked for some bread. His uniform was in rags, his boots broken, and his face, unshaven and unwashed, was haggard.

"Sit down", Ferdinand said, and went off to get some broth from the cook, who was used to visitors of this kind. When the boy came back, Mother Barat was on her knees poking the dying fire into a warm blaze.

"That will be better", she was saying, and the man held out his numbed fingers to the flames and rubbed them, but the look in his eyes still frightened the boy.

"Jolly good fire", Ferdinand said, trying to break the awkwardness he felt by speaking. "A fire's a very fine thing, I think."

The soldier turned and his eyes seemed haunted.

"No, son, fire is dreadful—if you had seen it as I saw it, leaping from house to house as the Russians fired Moscow, running up the church steeples as the bells rang out in frenzy, turning the shelter we had counted on for the winter into a smoking blackened ruin, you would say fire is dreadful, dreadful—a scourge of God."

He was silent. Mother Barat placed beside him a soft piece of the roll she had cut.

"God's scourge—yes, but the mercies of God are everlasting, and our confidence in Him must be everlasting too", she said.

The man stared at her, then his fist crashed down on the table.

"I am not afraid of any man", he cried. "but when God acts, I grow fearful. After the fire came the cold. I saw men drop down in the snow with no wound to slay them—I saw their hands stiffen and their eyes glaze, and they fell like logs—I saw men weeping, weeping like children, as they trailed through the snow and huddled together at night with the frost riming their hair and beards. And I tell you I am afraid to fight against God. It was not men that routed us, the Emperor was defeated by no armies—it was God defending His Church, God showing His might in answer to the prayers of His Vicar on earth. What crazy ambition led Napoleon to take Pius VII prisoner? We thought in our folly to make a meal of the Pope, and we've found men die of that food."

He stopped and shivered. Mother Barat slipped off the little shawl she was wearing and tucked it into the man's coat round his shoulders.

"Drink up your broth", she ordered, and smiled to see him obey. As the warm drink vanished down his throat, he smiled at her in turn and Ferdinand thought the strained look had gone from his face. When he rose to go, Mother Barat said to him softly, "Suffering ought to be very precious to us if we have the eyes of faith. The best treasure that Jesus left us was His Cross."

The soldier shrugged his tattered shoulders.

"Perhaps—I don't know. Well, you've been very kind to me." He pulled his rags round him. "I can't repay you except by a bit of advice that has cost me much to learn. You can't build empires by yourself—you can't lay your plans just to suit yourself and hope to wangle things with the Almighty. You can't fight against God, and if He wants a thing, you can as soon stop the fire that burnt Moscow as prevent Him from getting His way."

When he had gone, Ferdinand said thoughtfully, "Madame Barat, isn't that what the Greeks called '*hubris*' —when a man's ambition leads him on from conquest to conquest until he thinks he can do without the gods, and then at the height of his power, he falls—like Agamemnon and Xerxes?"

"Yes", she answered him, "and the Scriptures call it pride—by that sin the angels fell. Oh, Ferdinand, let's pray always to be humble."

Rome in the early days of August, 1815, was stifling but M. de Saint-Estève was so busy putting the finishing touches to a long letter he was writing that he scarcely noticed the heat. At last he laid down his quill and with a sigh of satisfaction leant back in his chair. There was so much to feel satisfied about. The fall of the Empire had given him the chance of this appointment under the new Government as secretary to the French Ambassador in the Holy City, with all its opportunities of meeting ministers and ecclesiastics who really mattered. His repute as the able founder of a new religious order was surely, if slowly, growing, and now that he had persuaded Mother Baudemont and some of her daughters to leave Amiens and come to the house he had opened in Rome, no one could doubt that he was right when he modestly stated that the Apostolines under his direction had a great work to do for the Church. It was of course a pity that the Superior of the house at Ghent had become so disturbed by his moves that she had broken both with him and with Mother Barat, but although some of the nuns had returned to Amiens, even there he had still correspondence with quite a number who he thought would be ready to throw over the authority of the so-called Mother General as soon as he gave the stimulus. It was a very satisfactory thing too that the Jesuits had been restored to France—that meant that Father Varin was safely out of the way making his noviceship, and the brother, Louis Barat, who was a potential ally, was also tied.[1] Left to herself, Sophie Barat would not prove much of an obstacle to his plans. What could she do with her Rules and Constitutions when he was actually here in Rome, on the spot, to get the approbation of the Holy See for his own compilation? Already he had the ear of influential people at the Vatican. He was becoming a somebody, esteem would lead to a proper recognition of his gifts—preferment would mean more opportunity to assert himself—as bishop what might he not accomplish—he checked himself as the red hat of a cardinal came before his

[1] Louis Barat, like his superior, Joseph Varin, became a Jesuit. A most zealous priest, he gave many missions in France, and, while stationed at Bordeaux, was able to make arrangements for the departure of Blessed Philippine Duchesne and her companions to America, and to give the little band his blessing. It is pleasant to read in an early letter from Mother Duchesne to his sister that the children in their first free school in Louisiana had learned to sing many of the hymns of Father Barat, especially one to the Sacred Heart. He died in 1845 at the age of seventy-seven, after a long and painful illness. "Our Lord wants me like this", he said. "He knows what is best." He sent a special last benediction to his sister and her Society, making, like her, a generous sacrifice of a last meeting. She learnt of his death while she was at Turin. "This news has pierced my poor heart", she wrote. "I so much wanted to see him again for a few minutes . . . but my grief is softened by the well-founded hope of the happiness that a soul so faithful to God must enjoy in Heaven."

eyes, and turned to the immediate satisfaction of his letter. He had put his opening points neatly—when Mother Barat began this screed from an unknown correspondent, she could not but be struck by the apparent good will which prompted the writer to warn her that if she persisted in preventing her daughters from carrying out the project of M. de Saint-Estève, she would incur *ipso facto* excommunication, by not submitting to the decisions of the Holy See. He re-read his words: "How, if you refuse, can you hope for an approval or even toleration from the Pope? To use his own words, 'He will suppress you to prevent scandal and division'."That sounded pontifical—and was a point likely to go home, seeing that Sophie Barat had always professed to be loyal to the Papacy. And then, the perfect end. "Your fate is in your hands. If you will forward to me your act of adhesion to the Convent in Rome, I will use it discreetly, and will undertake to transmit to you the reply of the first Superior, who cannot but be full of consideration for you."

M. de Saint-Estève took up his quill, dipped it in the inkwell, and with a smile signed his letter. "Stephanelli", he wrote, and added, "Roman College, Rome, August 5th, 1815". That would settle any tomfooleries of passive resistance once and for all. He enjoyed in anticipation receiving generously and with full forgiveness the meek apologies of the one-time Mother General, who would take her place again as a useful teacher of his Institute. He could afford to make a show of sheltering the erring lamb returning to the fold. He would have to see to it that Mother Baudemont adopted the same attitude, but perhaps with a little more firmness. She would need to keep Sophie Barat in her place for the sake of the weaker members who still wavered in their allegiance.

To Sophie the letter seemed final. Father Varin held out no hopes. If the Holy Father had spoken, there was nothing further to do, and she agreed. "It is the death sentence passed on our little Society", she said to holy Abbé Perreau, the secretary of the Grand Almoner of France, when he called on her one day. "It is right that the devil should be let loose upon us, and that we should die. And yet—though I know this sentence is the end, I cannot help thinking that from the ashes of our endeavour the Society of the Sacred Heart will rise again. 'The grain of wheat must die before it bear fruit'."

"May I have a look at this death warrant of yours?" the Abbé asked, and he put on his spectacles as Sophie handed him the letter. "Hmm, who is this Stephanelli, I should like to know? I thought I was familiar with all the names of the Roman College, and I don't recollect this one. The style does not ring true. I have had too much correspondence with Rome not to feel that this letter is not genuine. Keep your confidence still. I shall make inquiries at Rome myself. And now I shall say to you what our good friend Father Varin has for once forgotten to say to you, though he is so fond of it: 'Courage and confidence'."[1]

There came a day in Rome when the French ambassador had a heart-to-heart talk with his secretary, M. de Saint-Estève, in which he did most of the talking. At the end of the interview the secretary gathered up his belongings and left the embassy, not to return. In a few days he was journeying back to France, and he did not even call on the Rome house of the Apostolines to say good-bye to Mother Baudemont. The passage in the diligence over the Mont-Cenis pass seemed to him very cold. No doubt it was the

[1] Father Varin remained a faithful friend and counsellor till his death in 1850. As an old man, he delighted in visiting the novices at Conflans near Paris. His last words to them re-echoed those he had spoken so often when their Mother Foundress was beginning her religious life. "My daughters, always courage and confidence." After the expulsion of religious orders from France in the early part of this century, his remains were brought to England and are now buried in the chapel of the Sacred Heart Convent, Roehampton.

change after Roman warmth. He shivered as they dropped down into Lanslebourg, and heard French spoken again. The postilion looked with distaste at the Abbé as he got down from the carriage and made for the inn.

"Cold?" he asked. "Well, it's not my fault that there's snow in the wind. You ought to have come back from Moscow with the Grand Army—then you'd know what cold is." And he spat after the retreating form of M. de Saint-Estève.

Chapter XIII

RICH MAN, POOR MAN...

IN the last week of March, 1818, Mother Barat sat at her desk in the little house of the Society in Paris and wrote letters. Since the Pope had blessed the Rules and Constitutions drawn up at the château of Chevroz, there had been more than enough work to do. Foundations were being asked for on all sides, and not in France alone, and there was no lack of novices being trained to carry out the work. But as soon as they were ready to do the tasks that awaited them, the work spread and the demand for more religious grew.

"It's like always having empty pockets when you've a hunger like Gargantua's to satisfy", said one novice. "And it's strange that God sometimes gets someone all ready to do some job, and then lets her die."

"That is to remind us that He alone is rich enough to do all things—we must love our dependence on Him, and our own indigence", Mother Barat pointed out, and then set the novices to work as busily as if the whole success of the Society depended on their labours. "Don't forget we are poor people", she had reminded them.

She could not forget the fact herself as she went through letter after letter. Here was the house at Quimper with the bare minimum for subsistence—"Still, we can't send home little Thérèse because her parents can't pay her fees", she considered, "when the child's faith depends on our training.

I think we might be able to retrench here a little and send Quimper the extra. Sister Marguerite came with a plan for doing the children's laundry with the new sister novices —that would make the necessary saving."

As she turned to the next letter, the door opened quickly and her secretary, Mother Ducis, came in.

"Mother", she said, holding out an envelope, "this has come from Bordeaux—the messenger said that Mother Duchesne sailed for America on Holy Saturday."

Mother Barat took the letter and read it.

"Yes", she answered, "Mother Duchesne has gone at last—after more than twelve years of waiting."

"I think she must feel a bit like Jacob serving Laban seven years for the sake of Rachel—and they seemed but a few days because of the greatness of his love—now she has her heart's desire."

Mother Barat gave a little sigh.

"Why, I believe you wish it was you, Mother", cried Mother Ducis. "Do you envy her?"

"Indeed I do", was the reply. "My old attraction for the Missions is wide awake, but there's no chance of my sharing Mother Duchesne's lot. I am tied to this desk, worrying my head over money and financial matters while she will be suffering the real hardships that come from poverty."

Mother Ducis glanced up at the Mother General.

"Mother", she asked, "isn't there another kind of poverty besides not having money to buy things with? I mean, not possessing anything, or not holding on to anything? Wealth isn't just gold and silver, is it? When your father and your mother died, and you did not go to them because of our Rule of Enclosure, I said to myself, 'We are like poor people who haven't the journey money———' "

"No", Mother Barat interrupted, "say rather, 'We are

like someone who is so rich that we can ensure the best of care for our sick'—what more skilled physician than Our Lord, or what more loving nurse than Our Lady? We can count on their being there."

"Well, then", Mother Ducis pursued her point, "our friends are part of our wealth."

"And Mother Duchesne gives us all up", Mother Barat prompted her.

"I was going to say, you give up Mother Duchesne", retorted Mother Ducis. "And it's poverty, I think too, to give up what you want to do—like going on the Missions", she added to herself.

Mother Barat smiled.

"Go on thinking of the other things that you can give up or have taken from you, but don't forget also to rejoice when you feel the effects of lack of money as well, when it means that your dress or your food or your rest, or your lodging is really like that of a poor woman. And, come, Henriette, poor women have to work", Mother Barat finished with a laugh, and they got down to the task of dealing with the day's business.

"I suppose you will say it's poverty for a poet's daughter like you to be writing business letters, instead of verses", Mother Barat said at the end of two hours' work, teasingly.

"Poor people are grateful for any work they can get", Mother Ducis answered. "Now, what shall I write to the bank?"

Summer came and in July Mother Barat was off to open a new house in Chambéry. It was great fun, thought the new-fledged novice Helène du Tour, to be riding off from Grenoble in a procession that would do credit to a party of peasants out for the day. In front in a trap was the Mother General and one of her Reverend Mothers, with the Abbé from Chambéry urging on his horse over the mountain

roads like a Jehu. Jolting up against the respectable professed Mother in a second trap was Helène, but the carpenter who drove them was a very poor rival to the Abbé and
soon they had lost sight of even the dust of the first equipage.
With what laughter were they greeted when they caught up
at a village where they had stopped to bait the horses.

"Good", said the Abbé as the man came from the inn
with an armful of oats for the sweating animals, and a
loaf of bread and a bottle of wine. "They've earned their
dinner." And he went into the inn.

"For pity's sake, let me have some, too", Mother Barat
begged. The inn keeper broke off a hunk of bread while
the carpenter gallantly produced a glass from his coat and
poured out some of the wine. The Mother General took
them gratefully, while the horse paused from his eating to
rub his nose against her arm. The Abbé came from the
house.

"They can give us refreshment within", he said.

"Thank you", Mother Barat said gaily; "the others will
be very glad of it but I have had my dinner with the
horse." And she remained outside, playing with the
innkeeper's little son until they were ready to start again.

"I like this ride", Helène said to her companion. "It's
nicer than going in a diligence, because without a roof you
can see more. Besides, it makes me feel poorer."

"Poorer?" Her companion was surprised. "With all these
riches of God's creation to look at? Why, you'd miss them
all inside a coach, and you'd not hear the waterfall or smell
the freshness of the snows—you don't know when you're
well off."

Mother Barat was delighted that the house they had for
her at Chambéry was dedicated to Saint Clare. There was
no doubt that the building itself was devoted to poverty,
but with more holes now than holiness, for the carpenter

G

still had many repairs to make before the old convent was ready to be used by the new nuns. There was a farmer who had the ground floor for his use, the owner had not yet moved out from the first-floor rooms, so that the Religious had to climb up to the second floor.

"Well, we're all the nearer Heaven", remarked Hélène. Presently a bell rang, and the owner invited them down to a meal so fine and well served that Mother Barat sighed and shook her head.

"Saints did not act like this when they made their foundations", she said.

"But poor people do not refuse what is offered them", the Abbé said, as he came into the room bearing in his hands with great pride a large Savoyard cake on the top of which he had perched a rose bud. "And don't forget that Saint Clare made little sweet cakes for Saint Francis."

By the end of the week, they had everything in order, and had even managed to give beauty to the little room set apart for the chapel. Mother Barat reminded them of Father Varin's words, "Our Lord's first home was a stable and his first resting-place a manger. Let nothing be too good for what regards God and the service of the Altar: don't stint anything when you would help your neighbour or the children: but for yourselves, everything must be poor."

Then one morning the good Abbé arrived in great distress, anger and chagrin struggling for mastery as he blurted out:

"Mother Barat, why have you deceived me?—why could you not have been frank and open all along? Here have I been thinking your Society had the blessing of the Pope and now I find that you are no better than schismatics, broken away from the parent branch, going even against the direct instructions of the Holy Father——"

"But, Father," said Mother Barat bewildered, "what is making you think all this?"

"What indeed", he said, still bridling. "It's all about the town—they are saying the bishop himself has been undeceived only just in time—that it was providential that Mother Baudemont should have chosen this moment to come from Rome where her house is the only one approved and recognised by the Pope——"

"Father," Mother Barat began to see daylight, "you may be listening just to false reports——"

He interrupted her. "False reports? No, I know that Mother Baudemont has been received by the Governor, and the Countess his wife has presented her to His Lordship the Bishop. How could you have tricked me so? And I'm all the sorrier about it because I was sure you were the right person for this school", he added sadly as he went out.

Helène came in from her work with the carpenter.

"Mother, Jacques is very downcast this morning. He has been telling me that the two ladies who arrived the other day in the diligence from Rome haven't left you a shred of reputation—the gossip is all through the town that they alone are authorised to make foundations and that you are therefore nothing more than an adventuress, who will shortly be sent packing. He says *he* doesn't believe it, but he's very upset. Mother, what can we do?" Helène was close to tears.

Her Mother smiled at her.

"Here you are living in a convent that once belonged to Poor Clares, and you don't know what St. Francis said about the happiness of being so poor in honour that all men despise you?" she said. "There's nothing better to do, my child, than pray. Thank God I can write, too, to the Abbé Perreau for proof of our position."

Before the answer came from the secretary of the Grand Almoner, Mother Baudemont had called on Sophie, and

in no pacific frame of mind. Her chief object was to get the
payment of a thousand francs which she said were her due
for the work done at Amiens. When she had gone, Sophie
collected together all her available money.

"It's not much", she remarked. "Three hundred francs
on account and I'll send the relics and books she claims as
soon as I can get them from Amiens. I don't want to wound
charity for the sake of money. Our Lord will make it up to
us——"

Helène wondered how, but her doubts were soon dis-
pelled. The Abbé Perreau was able more than to reinstate
the nuns in the eyes of the bishop, and the town soon saw
for itself that they had misjudged the case. Madame
Baudemont was not invited to stay with the Governor and
his wife on her return journey to Rome.

On the day she left Chambéry, with the house in full
working order, Mother Barat with Helène said good-bye
to a very disconsolate carpenter.

"Madame", he said, and brought his hand from behind
his back, "I wanted to give you something—here's a bit of
edelweiss—straight from the mountains of Savoy—a friend
of mine was climbing and got it at the snow-line—here you
are."

Mother Barat was touched and her gratitude pleased
the man. He bowed himself away and indulged in an
orgy of sawing to soothe his feelings.

"Edelweiss doesn't look beautiful down in the town",
Helène remarked. "It gets dirty and tawdry-looking—you
want to see it high up on the mountains where even the
grass does not grow, and there's nothing but the virgin snow
and the cold air and the sun of God—it's wonderful, isn't
it, Mother, how it seems to flourish best when it has
nothing——?"

"Does that make you think of something, Helène?"
Mother Barat asked. Helène paused before she replied:

"I suppose we should be whiter and more beautiful if we had nothing but the grace of God."

Two years later the fashionable circles in Paris had much to talk about.

"Is it true that the Nuns of the Sacred Heart have actually bought the Hôtel Biron?—have they established themselves in the very neighbourhood of Les Invalides?" Madame Catherine Besier asked the Duchess of Charost.

"And why not?" that old lady answered her. "They were squeezed to death in their old Paris quarters."

"But the Hôtel Biron!" Madame Besier would not be put off. "It is the height of luxury—and I thought these Religious were supposed to be poor", she added, smoothing her silk skirts.

"They say the King has deigned to take an interest in the whole affair", Mlle. Lemenuisier said, maliciously. "We are flying high it seems. The Mother General knows apparently how to get the ear of the great—I understand the Duchess of Berry and the Duchess of Angoulême have been to visit them—quite like old times in the Hôtel."

"Not a bit of it!" the Countess of Charost retorted. "When I lived there, there were mirrors and pictures and murals and gildings—you won't find them anywhere, and the children are being trained to look for something other than outward show of nobility."

"They say the novices moved in on the feast of Saint Francis of Assisi—rather a queer day to choose, don't you think?" Mlle. Lemenuisier went on. "There is the story of his refusing to lodge in a newly-founded house where there was too much comfort, and going off to spend the night in a barn."

The Duke of Montmorency had joined the group as she spoke.

"It's all right, Mademoiselle", he assured her. "The

little Poor Man would find his bearings straight away and
make for the servants' quarters where Mother Barat and her
daughters lodge. I am going to the Hôtel Biron now if you
would care to come to see for yourself."

When the carriage put them down before the great
building, Mlle. Lemenuisier could not forbear to remark
that she would not be surprised to find flunkeys still going
about. The Duke smiled, and the two went through the
open door. A nun was busy sweeping the lodge, her habit
tucked up in a business-like way, and her broom going
carefully and swiftly across the floor and into all the corners.
Mlle. Lemenuisier watched critically.

"Well, at least they have taught the lay-sisters to do
their work thoroughly", she remarked, but the Duke was
not listening to her. As the nun turned, he cried out:

"Ah, Madame Barat, I've caught you. What are you
doing there?"

"What I ought to have been doing all my life", the
Mother General replied, "if I had been left in my right
place." Then she put down the broom and smilingly
greeted her visitors.

When they had gone, three of the older children came to
her door.

"Well, Louise?" she asked their spokesman. "Do you
want something?" Louise tossed her head, and looked
boldly at Mother Barat.

"It's like this", she began. "We want to let you know
that we don't want to be taught by Mother Closset. She's
just a nobody, with no family at all, and we're all sure she
can't teach us anything and we don't intend to give her a
chance."

Mother Barat looked at them. For all of them, pride of
birth was the corner stone of their conduct, spoiling their
generous qualities.

"I see", she said, "Now listen. God places people in authority and others respect them because they represent God. That is His Law. But you, children, see things differently, since you wish all your mistresses to be well-born. As this is so, you will see me no more, for my family has absolutely no claims whatever to nobility. And so, good-bye."

She indicated that the interview was over, but the children, looking at each other in consternation, stood rooted to the ground.

"What, Mother Barat? We'll never see you again?" cried the first.

"Oh, we couldn't get on without you!" Horror was in the voice of the second.

"Oh, Mother——" Louise burst into tears.

Mother Barat waited. The apology was not long in coming when the tears had subsided, and the lesson was ended.

"Go away now, children, and learn to appreciate those qualities in others that make them truly noble in the eyes of God", she said, "and don't think so much of the judgments of the world." Then as they filed out, she added, "What is that you are making with that wool, Louise?" Louise blushed. "It was a surprise for you, Mother. We're all making dresses and things for you to give to the poor babies."

"So you are my children after all!" Mother Barat cried in delight, and the three went away content.

There came a knock at the door, and a novice entered.

"You wanted me, Mother?" she asked.

"Yes", Mother Barat looked severe. "I heard you yesterday grumble at the patched habit you are wearing. You will go straight away and change into your secular dress. You are not worthy to wear the humble livery of Our Lord if your standards are still so worldly."

"Oh, Mother", the novice began, "I didn't really mean it—please let me keep my habit."

But Mother Barat was inexorable, and the flounces and furbelows of the world had to be worn for three days. Yet it was well worth the penance, and later the novice was grateful that she was made to see so clearly that poverty should be loved with the love that made Christ choose to be born and die in its midst.

It was from Paris in 1829 that Mother Ducis, the Mother General's secretary, was writing to Mother Grosier: Henriette would be anxious to get news of Sophie's accident.

"I am sure you will rejoice with me that the doctors do not now think that the injury done to Mother Barat's foot by her fall will necessitate amputation. But they order complete rest for it. We have therefore had a wicker basket made—rather like the kind a dog would rest in, only of course much larger—and in this she can lie and yet be moved from place to place. Sister Dubois is strong enough to move it about—but you know how absent-minded she is, and I am afraid she sometimes forgets our Mother."

She paused and her thoughts ran back over the years that she had known Sophie. Then she wrote again.

"How strangely God seems to deal with her. You would think that with all the foundations she has to make, she would need robust health and yet He takes it away and leaves her a beggar's pittance. Do you remember how ill she was at Amiens, at Grenoble, and at Cuignières, how we have twice thought that we should lose her, and now there is this accident that threatens to cripple her for ever. When I commiserated with her, she said, 'God will come to my aid.' I am afraid I cannot think of her future sufferings without sorrow, but she laughs and says life will go quickly, and it is not worth while to care a great deal about the inn where we pass so short a time when we have a lovely and lasting home in Heaven. Well, I suppose health is one of our possessions—and the self-will that would arrange things just as we would like them for those we love", she added, remembering how Mother Barat had told her to think what poverty could mean, and what things she could give up.

After the nine-thirty class, the bell rang for a short play interval. Claire slipped out of the Junior School room and ran along to the chapel. At the door she smoothed down her black pinafore and put on her veil. She fumbled in her pockets, but her gloves were not here. "Bother!" she thought, and then, "but Jesus won't mind if I don't have them on, and it's only a little tiny visit I'm going to make, and I can't wait any longer to thank Him for letting me make my First Communion next month."

She pushed open the heavy door and tiptoed up the chapel to the altar-rails and knelt there. After a minute she heard someone calling softly, "Claire, Claire".

"Who is it?" she wondered. "Where does the voice come from? It sounds quite close."

She looked along to the end of the rails and in a flash had scrambled down to where a large wicker basket lay beside the steps.

"Mother Barat!" she said excitedly, "I'm going to be a chalice for Our Lord like you told us, next month, and I'm going to try and make myself all rich and gold inside, by being good and—and—eating cabbage—and helping people—so as to make up for the draughts and cobwebs of the stable when He came first—and—and Mother Ducis told me to make a big hole in my heart—she said, the bigger the hole, the more God could put in—and. . . ." She stopped, remembering Mother Barat had called her. "Do you want anything, Mother?"

The Mother General smiled.

"Well, Claire, perhaps you could find someone to take me away—I think they have forgotten me." Claire's eyes opened. "Have you been here ever since Mass?"

Mother Barat nodded.

"Oh, how dreadful!" Claire was filled with indignation. "Why, you haven't had your breakfast!"

She turned to hurry away, and then added: "How could they! How could they leave you for so long with nothing!"

Mother Barat watched her little chubby legs run down the chapel, then she looked again at the Tabernacle.

"With nothing?" she thought. "No, with everything."

Chapter XIV

QUIA PECCAVIMUS

THE conflagration started by the French Revolution had not burnt itself out. In 1830 the smouldering fires flared up again, and very soon there were barricades in the streets of Paris, and fighting had begun.

Mother Anna de Constantin was young and strong and stout-hearted. That was why she was in charge of a sick nun and two sisters, in the house the Archbishop of Paris had lent them near his seminary in the village of Conflans a few miles outside the city. A post of honour and responsibility—but it seemed such a safe place to be in!

"A week ago Father Varin came and asked us if we were ready for execution", she reminded herself regretfully. "He told us to rejoice in the midst of trials and possible revolution, and I thought on Monday, when the police closed the printing presses and the mob began to gather and shout, that there really was going to be a chance of martyrdom—and here am I now, well out of Paris, with nothing more exciting to do than to see my invalid gets her medicine at the right time."

There was a rumble of wheels—a carriage was drawing up before the door. Mother de Constantin pulled open the shutters that kept out the hot July sunshine and looked to see who it could be. She caught sight of a pair of crutches.

"Why, it's Mother Barat!" she cried, and went like a flash to let her in.

"The Mothers in Paris have sent me away because the barricades are up and fighting has begun, and I am such a cripple I should only be in the way if the Hôtel Biron was attacked," Mother Barat excused herself.

"What has been happening the last two days?" Anna inquired anxiously.

"On the 27th, most of the children were taken home by their parents, as the crowds in the streets were growing more and more threatening. The King called out his troops to restore order, but the troops have refused to fire on the mob and have deserted their colours. This morning we were awakened by the roar of cannon—the Revolution is in full progress", Mother Barat ended, her eyes full of tears.

The night brought no rest. Anna, waking from time to time, could hear Mother Barat praying aloud.

"Lord, protect Your Church—save its ministers——". Over and over again came the petition and the sigh, "Lord, we have sinned, yet save us!"

When morning dawned, Sister Rosalie had news from the gardener.

"He's just off", she said. "He says everyone has gone away from the seminary, and he's going too—it's much too dangerous to stay here."

Mother de Constantin's spirits rose at the prospect of danger, but the sun still shone brightly overhead and the bees buzzed in the garden and the trees stirred lazily in the hot breeze.

Then at two a noise of shouting was heard. Along the road came a rabble of some three hundred youths from the veterinary school. They stopped at the iron gate that led into the court-yard of the house.

"Here, boys", cried one. "We'll get into the seminary this way."

He shook at the bars, while the others round about encouraged him with cries of, "Down with the priests! Death to the lot of them!"

"Curse it, I can't shift the gate", he said after a time. "And it's too high to climb."

"Set fire to the house!" someone called out, and the cry was taken up and re-echoed.

"Set fire to it—go on, set fire to it."

From behind the closed shutters, Anna waited with beating heart, wondering what the hush meant that had fallen on them. Was someone producing flint and tinder? How did you begin to set fire to a house? Perhaps they were going round with gunpowder?

Suddenly there was a loud shout. "Oh, chuck it, boys— let's try the other way into the seminary."

There was an answering murmur of voices, someone struck up the Marseillaise, and the noisy crowd was off once more.

"Martyrdom missed again", thought Anna ruefully, but her heart was beating with gratitude. The invalid Mother called her.

"Anna", she said, "you and Sister Rosalie must put on secular dress and go down to the village and see if you can get us shelter there."

Secular dress! It was a good thing that Sister Rosalie had only just become a novice—she still had her own clothes, but what was Mother de Constantin to do?

"Where there's a will there's a way", she told herself, and searched round till she found an old brown skirt with some patches on it.

"I'll wear a white jacket with this, and put this fichu with pink stripes round my neck. Now then, a nightcap on my head, tied round with this blue and white handkerchief, and knotted by my left ear, and I look like one of the working women of Paris. What about my own black apron to put the finishing touch? Come along, Sister Rosalie, let's see if our own Mothers can recognise us."

Mother Barat, in spite of her anxieties, laughed heartily,

and reinforced by her blessing, Anna went off down the road to the village. As they turned up one long, lonely, narrow street, they came upon a stout little man, bareheaded, his shirt sleeves rolled up, shaking his fists and talking fiercely to himself.

"Saint Joseph, help us—here's one of the revolutionaries!" Anna said. "Don't say anything to him if he insults us, Sister Rosalie."

They drew near him with some trepidation, but he only said a loud "Good-day, ladies", as they passed.

"One danger over!" Anna whispered happily.

"Shall we try this house?" Sister Rosalie asked as they came on a large cottage, and they knocked at the door.

"We should like to take you in, but we haven't any room", said the woman who opened the door to them. "Try Madame Sougard up the road—there's only herself and her son who is dying."

But Madame Sougard refused. "Can't you see I've troubles enough—try somewhere else."

At the end of the afternoon, they seemed to have tried everywhere, and always the answer was the same.

"Well, Sister Rosalie, we'll understand better now what Bethlehem meant to Saint Joseph", Anna said. "Come on, this is the last house."

She rang the bell and waited. The door was flung open vigorously, and they found themselves face to face with the man in shirt sleeves!

"Come in, ladies", he said in his big voice, before they could run away. "I'm sorry the revolutionaries had made me lose my temper when I saw you earlier—you want shelter? Come with me and we'll ask my mistress, Madame Saladin."

He led them into a large room. At the far end, seated in an armchair, was a little old lady. She glanced up from her book and gazed with surprise at her two visitors.

"I forgot we looked such guys", Anna thought, suddenly conscious of the nightcap with its blue and white knot, and the patches on her skirt. "No wonder she's sending her maid to question us. Well, Saint Joseph, inspire me to say the right thing. I wonder if she'll believe me if I tell her the truth?"

It took little time to tell the maid their errand, but longer for her to get it into the head of her mistress, who was very deaf.

"They want to be nuns?" she said suspiciously, when the girl had repeated their information.

"They are nuns", the maid shouted.

"What? In that attire?" Madame Saladin sounded unbelieving.

"They're escaping——" began the maid again.

"I won't have anything to do with escaping nuns." The old lady shut her lips firmly.

"Escaping from the revolutionaries", the maid raised her voice.

"Why didn't you say so before? And they'll be wanting shelter. Really, Marcelle, you are very slow in understanding a situation." Madame Saladin rose from her chair and greeted her visitors. "My whole house is yours. The first floor isn't used, you'll find beds and mattresses—here is my kitchen, my garden, take anything you please. It is an honour to shelter those who are persecuted for Our Lord's sake."

Only when she was safe in bed that night, full of gratitude to God for having brought Mother Barat to this secure refuge, did Anna remember that the palm had again eluded her grasp.

On the 31st a messenger from the Hôtel Biron discovered their whereabouts.

"Paris is quieter now", this good woman told them. "But, Lord, what times we've had! They barricaded all round the Hôtel and you couldn't hear yourself think, what with the cannons and firing and singing the Marseillaise, and the worst of it was, no one could know what exactly was happening. We thought one day, when a man in a great-coat and a cockade made his way into the house, that we were going to be turned out by the revolutionaries, but bless you, it was only Father Varin come to see if we were all right. The sisters went on with their washing-day, but when the bullets began to fly across the garden, they brought the washing in. The Swiss Guard were fighting like fury, but it's all up now—the King's gone, they say, and they talk about having Louis-Philippe instead— anyhow, Paris is getting back into working order—here's the newspaper, the *Constitutional*, to prove it—and the Mothers say you'd all be safer back there. I've brought some secular dresses, and the man here says he can get a two-wheeled cart to take you."

There was laughter as the two Mothers put on little poke bonnets and large shawls and climbed into their chariot, with one of the sisters. Madame Saladin was sorry to see them go.

"I love your Mother General", she said to Anna as she set off on foot with Sister Rosalie. "She's done me a lot of good."

At the Saracen's Head Inn on the Paris road, Jean-Baptiste, the plumber's mate, was quite sure he thought the Revolution was a good thing.

"It's giving us the Charter of our liberties", he told his friend as he drained the first glass of wine in its honour.

"Long live the Revolution and down with Charles X!" he said at the end of the second bottle.

"It's the Revolution that'll set us all up", he said hopefully but vaguely as he wiped his mouth after the third bottle. "So long!" and he went out into the hot road.

"Sapristi!" he muttered. "There's a revolution in my legs. I'll just lean against this tree a minute. What's this coming along the road? A carriage? Didn't I say the Revolution would set us all up? Hi! Mate!" he hailed the driver, who pulled up. "Let me get up alongside of you". Without waiting for permission, he climbed up on the driver's seat and began to shout, "Long live the Charter! Long live the Revolution! Long live what you jolly well like!"

Inside the cart, Mother Barat began to laugh. Jean-Baptiste glanced down, and liked the look of her twinkling eyes.

"Good day, good Mother. I see you've hurt your foot. That's a pity, for this carriage won't be able to go very far. But don't get bothered about that—I'm strong and I'll carry you wherever you can't walk——" he raised his voice again, "Long live the Charter! Long live the Charter!"

"Sister", Mother Barat whispered across to the sister who was still fearful of revolutionary violence. "Courage and confidence! God has sent His Angel to give us safe-conduct. We sound now like good partisans of the Revolution."

At the barrier they were stopped.

"You can't enter Paris", said the official. Mother Barat produced *The Constitutional*. . . .

"It says here we may", she pointed out. Greedy for news, the guards crowded round her.

"Take the newspaper yourselves", she said, and smiling their thanks, they let her through. Soon the cart stopped again.

"Can't go any further", the driver said. "There are trees down blocking the road."

Jean-Baptiste climbed from his perch. The revolution seemed to be over in his legs.

"Come on, Mother", he said and helped Mother Barat

H

out. "This way—take care of that pool—here, wait a minute, I'll get a plank and help the ladies across. No, Mother, I'll have to carry you."

And he picked her up, crutches and all, and saw her safely through the barricades.

"The Angels shall bear thee in their arms lest thou dash thy foot against a stone", the sister whispered and thought what strange angels God did provide, as Jean-Baptiste went off at last and they heard his shouts of "Long live the Charter!" dying in the distance.

In the months that followed, Mother Barat saw the work of many of her houses in France wrecked and her children scattered. But God opened a refuge for her novices in Switzerland, and she felt that His help was with her however dark the days might be.

"God wants us to suffer", she wrote to Mother Henriette Grosier struggling to keep Poitiers safe for the Society. "Alas! His Heart is so filled with bitterness that it is only just that we should taste some drop of it."

But Henriette shook her head sadly when she read the letter.

"And all this time there is the pain in Mother Barat's lame foot like an animal gnawing the bone. We must suffer—*Quia peccavimus*—because we have sinned, she says. Ah well, I suppose the saints help to bear the burden of our sins."

The peace that Mother Barat had found for her novices among the Swiss mountains was not to be hers. One day the friendly parish priest called with a newspaper.

"Listen to this, Madame", he said and read out: " 'An army of some five hundred nuns, led by their Mother General, has recently invaded our country', the special correspondent writes, and here is the editor pointing out the danger if she is allowed to remain on Swiss territory.

Believe me, if you want your daughters to be able to stay, you had better go."

Then came the news that cholera had broken out in Paris and other large cities.

"My sins, our sins, the sins of Paris, of France, of Europe, of the world—alas, we have all deserved to suffer", thought Mother Barat, her heart torn with anxiety for her daughters, and filled with compassion for the suffering. "We must all bow our heads beneath this scourge and humble ourselves, because we have sinned."

Then, like the Good Samaritan, she helped to gather up the victims—surely there was room at the Hôtel Biron for twenty little orphans? On the feast of the Sacred Heart they were installed, nuns and children sharing her joy in helping to provide for them, and she wondered, "Will not the outpouring of charity turn aside the punishment due to God's justice?"

In May 1832, the superior of Turin, Mother de Limminghe, urged her to see a famous Italian surgeon.

"It's over three years since you injured your foot, and no treatment has done it any good", she pointed out. "It may well be that it is now incurable, but you ought not for our sakes", she added tactically, "to neglect the possibility of a cure". And so Mother Barat consented at length to go to Turin.

Journeying along in May by the blue Mediterranean promised to be lovely. The sun shone merrily on the golden mimosa as the carriage that had brought them from Aix-en-Provence pulled up at the Pont du Var on the road to Nice. Two guards peered in while a third ordered the driver to come down. A crowd began gathering.

"That's her, right enough", they heard a man say.

"I'm not so sure", a second voice cried.

"I couldn't possibly be mistaken", a third roundly affirmed.

"Mother, do see what this is all about", Mother Barat asked, and Mother de Limminghe put her head out of the carriage window.

"What is happening?" she began.

"Get out, madame", said one of the soldiers, and hustled her into the guard-house. The commissioner of police there rose to his feet.

"Madame, I place you under arrest."

"But why?"

"Madame the Duchess of Berry does not need to ask that—when she has been trying to overthrow the work of the Revolution of 1830."

"But I am not the Duchess——"

The man smiled incredulously. Mother de Limminghe drew out her passport. The man glanced at it and handed it back.

"You will see, Madame the Duchess, that it is not quite in order. It is therefore no good pretending you are superior of a convent in Turin."

"Take me to the mayor", Mother de Limminghe ordered, and she set off with an escort. But the mayor would not help.

"Take me to the Sardinian consul", Mother de Limminghe requested next, but the consul was at dinner and kept her waiting in the street, and then did not believe her tale. Back she came, with a growing escort of ragged urchins and curious idlers, to the carriage where Mother Barat had patiently waited as the afternoon wore on.

"Mother", she said, "you had better go on to Turin—it's getting so late and you haven't had a meal today."

"Go away and leave you!" Mother Barat cried in astonishment. "What do you take your Mother for?"

She gathered up her crutches and climbed out of the carriage.

"I am going to this police commissioner", she said. The little crowd followed, nudging each other.

"Who's she?"

"Do you think that's the Duchess of Angoulême?"

"She'll get no change out of the police."

"Lock 'em both up, he will."

They gazed at the outside of the guard-house, enjoying their dire speculations as to the fate of political prisoners.

But they would have rubbed their eyes half an hour later to see the stern, unbending Arm of the Law bring into his private room with his very own hands two boiled eggs, which he placed with a flourish before Mother Barat, whom he had seated in his own particular chair.

"Madame", he said, "pray accept these in token of my regret over this misunderstanding. If only my men had had the sense to address themselves to you in the first place——"

"Monsieur, do not worry—I should not then have had the pleasure of this meeting", Mother Barat assured him, and as he withdrew, "Mother de Limminghe, we must give him the two bottles of wine they gave us at Aix—all's well that ends well."

"How did you manage him?" asked the bewildered Mother de Limminghe.

"Humility is a needle that mends many a hole", Mother Barat answered with a laugh.

It was midnight before they reached Nice, but the next day they were off again.

"You'd think the Devil himself was trying to keep us from Turin", said Mother de Limminghe, as their carriage reached the top of the Col de Tenda, and they found deep snow on the other side.

"You'll have to walk", the men told the passengers, as they slung the body from the wheels and placed it on sledge runners. "The lame lady'll have to stay inside—

she'll not be able to manage the snow with those crutches."

Struggling through the deep drifts, Mother de Limminghe watched with horror the quick descent of the carriage, the horses plunging and slipping, the white spray rising, the whole swaying and lurching as sharp hairpin bends were turned. It was a relief to catch up again where the snow had ended, and to find Mother Barat smiling her thanks to the drivers.

"Only a few more miles now", thought the anxious superior of Turin, as she observed dark clouds gathering and heard the rumble of thunder. "Courage and confidence!" Mother Barat reminded her as the storm burst and the hail beat down. "God and His good angels can help us and bring us safe home at last."

And when the storm was over, they found a warm welcome in Turin.

Some days later, the Mistress General of the School was speaking to the Children of Mary.

"You asked Our Lady for a miracle—you prayed, you and all the school, that she would cure Mother Barat's foot. The surgeon found a dislocation in the bones of a finger and a half in width. He feared the damage was irremediable, but he had faith in your prayers, my dear children. Today he tried an operation—by one movement of his hands he has set the bones right. Now be off, all of you, and thank Our Lady."

"How good God is!" Mother Barat was thinking as she walked without her crutches into the chapel and knelt before the Tabernacle. "You send trials, dear Lord, but You help too. You punish, but You forgive. You restore more than You take away. If we but knew Your Heart, how we should love You!"

Chapter XV

SED ANGELI

L UNCH time after being allowed to see a ceremony of
  postulants taking the habit! The Junior School
children were full of importance and delight. Tongues
were so busy discussing everything that Mother Barat
stopped as she passed the open door of the refectory, to
watch the happy scene.

"This is what I have lived for", she thought, "to gain
for the Church the souls of all these young children. How
well I remember in the early days, when we were planning
to form a little community who could adore the Heart of
Jesus night and day, how little it seemed we should accomplish, even if we were twenty-four nuns—and then I thought
that if we had young pupils whom we could teach to adore
and make reparation, how different it would be! And I
used to see hundreds and thousands of adorers in front of a
Monstrance lifted above the Church over the whole world
—I used to be alone before the Tabernacle, and yet I dreamed
of children to love our Eucharistic Lord in all the nations,
even to the uttermost parts of the earth."

A small English child attracted her attention. A nun
was standing at the table quite still as she kept her eye on the
needs of the children. The child glanced up at the tall back
beside her—the nun was not looking. Carefully the little
hand went out, carefully the edge of the veil was lifted,
carefully the corner was dipped into the child's cup of
cocoa, and as carefully dipped into a glass of water. Alas!
the nun turned at that moment, and the culprit was caught
red-handed.

"Jane!" the nun was surprised. "What on earth are you doing? That's not the way to behave. Go outside until you know what to do at table."

Jane climbed down from her chair and went slowly to the door. Mother Barat put out her hand and drew the child to her.

"What were you trying to do, Jane?" she asked.

Jane hung her head a moment, then looked up into the kind eyes that were watching her.

"I—I—I was trying to get a blessing", she whispered. "This morning the priest blessed the veils for the novices and blessed their habits, and I thought that if I put a bit of a blessed veil into my cocoa, I should get a bit of the blessing—because I don't get the blessings the others get because I'm not a Catholic. I didn't mean to be naughty."

Mother Barat bent and kissed her. "You weren't naughty, Jane, but don't worry, for Our Lord is blessing you all the time you are here, without your putting Mother Martin's veil in the cocoa. Run along in now and say you are sorry, and tell her all about it."

Jane went off, and Mother Barat returned to her room thinking, "There it is again! Our Lord won't let me alone. Always in my heart of hearts Jesus keeps reminding me that He wants us in England."

She picked up a letter from her desk.

"Here they are wanting us in Algiers—but I am much more anxious for England." She opened an atlas and studied a map of the British Isles. "A house in Roscrea", she mused. "Well, that is a beginning among English-speaking people, but it isn't England." She found Somerset. "Lord Clifford wants us there. It's not the right place for us, though he is pressing us so hard I don't know whether I shall be able to refuse him. Now London——" She paused and surveyed the situation like a good general. "We should be near the centre of things, in touch with many souls—God seems to have put this property of Berrymead into our way—I've no money and no nuns to spare, but I would be ready to make all sacrifices if God wants us there. There are all sorts of difficulties—the devil is working against us in England—but isn't that a sign that he fears us in that country? England—there is a nation that is made for great things."

The secretary came into the room.

"Mother, there is an Australian bishop waiting for you in the parlour." Mother Barat sighed. "Do you know what he is asking me for? He wants a convent in Sydney—how can I answer him? I haven't the nuns to send. How painful it is to have to refuse—when there are so many souls that we could lead to Our Lord. If only I had English-speaking nuns. Pray that we can take the love of Our Lord's Sacred Heart to England. She will give us missionaries in return."

In September 1842, Mother Barat sent Mother D'Avenas to London.

"God is forcing our hands", she said. "We must try to get Berrymead now, or lose the opportunity of a foundation in England for a long time."

Mother D'Avenas smiled ruefully as she journeyed across the Channel with no money in her possession, to buy a large property.

"I'm off to England to buy a house with not a sou in my pocket", she told Mr. Adams, the uncle of one of the nuns, whom she met travelling up to London.

"Indeed!" he said. "In that case, may I help? I can lend you the money, and your Mother General can pay it back when she is able."

"How true it is", she thought when she had thanked Mr. Adams, "that if God wants a thing, He will provide the means. If only we would trust Him more."

Mother Barat's anxieties were not over when Berrymead

was bought. "Whom can I send to be superior?" she asked herself as she thought of the gaps that death was making in the ranks of her first companions. "Mother Grosier's holiness would have attracted English people by its quietness, but she has just gone to God—Mother Deshayes' forthrightness would be liked, but she is over eighty now. I must have someone who is mature, solid, religious through and through, and calm. English people don't take to any other type. And then she must be someone who is wholeheartedly devoted to Our Lord's Sacred Heart."

It was Mother Merilhou who was at length sent over, and she took possession of the new house on December 8th, 1842. To the nuns then it was a day of devotion like any other day, but perhaps Our Lady smiled as she saw her Son's Sacred Heart spreading His kingdom further in her Dowry on the day when He would be glorified later in the Feast of her Immaculate Conception.

There were plenty of difficulties still. Against her better judgment the Mother General had sent another colony of religious to the house at Cannington in Somerset that Lord Clifford had fitted up for them. There was poverty; there were misunderstandings; the number of pupils grew very slowly. But good was being done and firm friends were being made, and never did she doubt that God was preparing a great work in England.

"I must go to England and see for myself", she told her council, and they protested at once. "But Mother, you are not well enough—you are only just recovering from an illness—the journey will be too much for you." Mother Barat smiled. "Pray for me then", she said. "Pray Our Lady and the Apostles so that the Holy Spirit may guide and enlighten us—and give me health for the visit."

It was at the end of May 1844 that she left the Mother-House in Paris with Mother D'Avenas, to go to England.

"For heaven's sake take care of yourself properly", said good Sister Marie, as she saw that the Mother General had everything she could possibly need for a perilous passage in an unknown land. "Here is a big thick shawl."

"But, Sister, what for?"

"Ah, Mother, they have fogs in London, and you must wrap up well. Oh dear, and they'll be making you eat roast beef and suet pudding and drink tea." Sister Marie shuddered at the prospect.

Bishop Morris met them at Abbeville, and saw them safely on to the packet-boat bound for Dover. He wanted Mother Barat's nuns so badly in his country that he watched over her journey with the foresight of a travel-agent. But his fears for her safety were unfounded. Up and down the deck she walked with him, with her eyes set on the distant cliffs growing whiter as they neared the shore, while the white-winged sea-gulls screamed overhead and swooped and flashed against the blue waters.

"This is what Father de la Colombière must have seen as he approached our land", the bishop said. "You know, it was a Queen of England who first petitioned the Holy Father for public devotion to Our Lord's Sacred Heart. I sometimes wonder whether her husband, James II, found some consolation for the loss of his throne in what the French Jesuit must have told him about Our Lord's revelations to Blessed Margaret Mary Alacoque."

With a trail of dirty smoke above and a trail of white foam below, the boat put into the harbour. Mother Barat looked with interest at the burly sailors as they fastened ropes and affixed the gangways. At last the moment for going on shore came. She stepped for the first time on to English soil. A wave of joy swept over her. England—the land that would do much for God!

"'Ere, ma'am, I'll tike yer bag. Goin' to the trine, ain't yer?" A porter had seized hold of her luggage. What was he saying? she wondered, but he was smiling at the little foreign lady with a friendliness that couldn't be mistaken. The bishop came up.

"That's right—to the London train", he told the man, who gathered up all the parcels and pushed a way for them through the crowd and found a carriage and saw them safely inside.

"French, are they?" he said to the bishop. "This'll be the first time they've gone in a train, I s'pose. We're a'ead of the Froggies there, ain't we?" and he glowed with patriotic pride.

Mother Barat smiled back—why did people say the English were so cold? This man's twinkle would warm up any heart.

"I see you're amused at our Cockney", the bishop said to her. "You'll be wanting to get a school for them, I can see—and you'll love them when you get them."

With much noise and belching smoke and hissing steam, the train moved out of the station. The red roofs of the town spun by, and green fields stretched away on both sides of the line. Looking out of the window, she saw strange hump-backed hills lying out into the sea like great monsters on guard. The blue sky overhead was flecked by white clouds as the sun shone down on lush meadows where the cattle moved slowly across to stand knee-deep in streams bordered with pollard willows. Hedges were white with hawthorn blossom, here and there they passed by orchards whose pink blossom, like rosy snow, waved on the branches. Hop-poles and oast-houses, cottages snug in tiny copses, farm houses with thatched roofs, distant blue wooded hills, stately spires and stout church towers. England was spreading herself before the enchanted eyes of the Mother General. Over a stile two children were climbing, rosy-cheeked and golden-haired, the little boy waving his greeting to the passing train, his sister in her clean pinafore gazing, poised on the topmost rung. Mother Barat caught her breath. The bishop followed her look.

"Do you feel like St. Gregory?" he asked her. "*Non Angli, sed Angeli*?"

"Ah no", she returned quickly. "This is now a country which can number martyrs among her sons and daughters —it has earned the faith. We can only pray that our generosity may be as great in God's service as theirs when they gave their lives for love of Him."

"You will have difficulties of your own", Bishop Morris reminded her.

"Yes," she answered, "but the bee does not make honey only from sweet-juiced flowers. Some bitter must be mixed with it, and it is that that makes it what it is."

"And how do we imitate the bees?" Mother D'Avenas asked.

"We must pass our sorrows and our joys, our bitter and our sweet, through the Heart of Our Lord, to make them the honey of our perfection", Mother Barat said, and thought of the work she still had to do before she could be worthy to take a place among the saints and martyrs.

At the London terminus the bishop saw them safely into a carriage. "This will take you all the way to Acton", he told them, and broke off to look at a gentleman who was passing by. "I thought for one moment that that was the celebrated Anglican preacher, Mr. Newman", he said in explanation. "He had something of his air of profound scholarship and real spirituality. There is someone that you could take into your prayers, Mother Barat. Some of us feel that he is very near the Church."

At last the carriage moved off, and rolled along the London streets. Past green parks they went. Mother D'Avenas pointed out distant views of grey towers rising with Gothic magic against the blue sky.

"That's Westminster Abbey", she said. "They told us

that there is still a statue of Our Lady above the North Door. The dome over there is St. Paul's." Soon the houses began to thin, and they found their road running between market gardens and green fields bright with buttercups and daisies, with every now and then a glimpse of a broad smooth-flowing river.

"There's the Thames", Mother D'Avenas pointed out, and then, as a village came into sight, she added with some excitement, "Why, there's Hammersmith, where we stayed when we first came to England. Look, Mother, where the roads meet at the Broadway, do you see the Benedictine Convent? The Lady Abbess told us that the house and grounds had always been Catholic. It belonged to one of the embassies—they say that Claude de la Colombière may have been there."

Mother Barat looked with great interest at the house surrounded with its high wall, and prayed that the burning love of the apostle of the Sacred Heart would fire her daughters too, in the land where he suffered so much. At length Acton came into view, and the carriage turned into a private drive and pulled up before an ivy-covered pseudo-Gothic porch. Fifteen young girls were standing there in immaculate order.

"There's the school", said Mother D'Avenas, and added with a sigh, "Fifteen only—what can we do with so few?"

She caught the Mother General's glance.

"Oh yes, Mother", she replied quickly to the unspoken comment. "The Apostles were only twelve."

It did not take long for the children to realise that they were truly dear to the heart of this ageing French Mother who had crossed the sea to see them.

"Isn't she kind?" they said to their own mistresses as they went off to bed that night. "We don't understand all she says, but you can just tell that she'd do anything for you. She's kind, that's what she is."

Up in her room, Mother Barat went to the window and looked out. Dimly she could see the heavy blooms of the rhododendrons in the garden, while the fresh scent of wallflowers rose from the flowerbeds below. In the gathering dusk of the early June day a thrush was singing on the bough of an oak tree, clear and joyful.

"I shall have to close the house in Somerset", she thought sadly. "It is like having two birds with only one wing apiece. When there is only Berrymead, it will have two wings and be able to fly."

A cuckoo cried from a distant wood. The chestnut spires stood up like candles waiting to be lit. Here and there in the houses of the neighbourhood lights appeared and shone out into the night.

"If only we can help to light the love of God", Mother Barat thought as she gazed out over England.

Chapter XVI

APPROBATION, 1845

GIULIA and Margherita followed Mother Barat up the dark staircase, and out on to the flat roof between the towers of the Trinità dei Monti. Giulia ran across to the stone balustrade, crying out in all the exuberance of her nine Italian years:

"Oh, Mother, I do so love being up here—right on the top of the church that is on the top of the hill! Doesn't everything look teeny-weeny down below—it makes me feel like an angel right up above the world—look, Margherita——" she pointed for her older sister's benefit, "you can just see where we went with those parcels Mother Barat sent us to take to Madame Baudemont. It took us ever such a long time, and yet from up here it doesn't seem any distance. Do you think things really look like that to the saints—do you, Mother Barat? Do they just get high enough with God and then see that things aren't as long and dreary as they seem?"

She paused as a new thought struck her. Wrinkling her nose she said, "I think I should have to be a real saint if I went to Madame Baudemont's silly little school—fancy, just two mistresses and only thirty children." Mother Barat turned to her quickly:

"Giulia, you mustn't be unkind in your judgements. Madame Baudemont and her friend are suffering a lot, and there is no one to help them. We must do what we can—pray for them too, my dear."

Giulia was off at a tangent. "Oh, look, there's the big watchdog from the Villa Lante!"

She watched the large animal walking sedately up the road and across the Piazza. Two ragged curs came running out from a doorway, but he disdained to notice them, and solemnly mounted the long flight of stone steps that led to the door of the Trinità.

"Isn't he clever, coming all the way by himself every day?" Giulia went on, her eyes seeking the convent roof on the opposite hill behind the Vatican, and following his route down past St. Peter's and through the maze of streets that led up again to the Trinità. "But won't he be sold when he goes out into the garden today, and finds you're not there?"

"I expect he'll find Mother Barat all the same", Margherita said. "Don't you remember the cat that brought all her kittens to Mother Barat to save them from being drowned? She discovered the right room. When you know what you want, you look till you find it—that's why I shall go to be a novice at the Villa Lante to-morrow."

Mother Barat smiled.

"And what a treasure you will find there—the Heart of God."

Giulia broke in again.

"Mother, the Holy Father says the Trinità and the Villa Lante are two strongholds where the Sacred Heart keeps watch and ward over Rome."

"It looks like that, doesn't it?" Margherita said. "You know, when you look on to all this cluster of roofs and see the domes rising here and there and St. Peter's in the midst, you seem to be looking down on something stable in the midst of time—it makes you want to call Rome the Eternal City—and then you notice here and there also the dark ruins of the city of the Caesars, and you are reminded that all that ancient glory has passed, and you wonder whether some day other people will be gazing down on the broken dome of Michelangelo and a smoke-blackened

I

city of the popes. And then I think, what if they do? Our Lord does not need bricks and mortar to preserve His Church."

"True", said Mother Barat. "If the love of the Sacred Heart is burnt into our souls, we shall have no need to be sad over the loss of material buildings."

"And then beyond the city are the hills—you can't just stay looking at the streets, can you?" Margherita asked.

"No, the horizon alone should bound our vision", Mother Barat answered. "And where can we get this breadth of view except in the Sacred Heart of Our Lord? He will plunge our nothingness into His immensity, and will transform us into Himself as iron in a furnace becomes like fire."

Giulia did not understand what she was talking about, but it made her feel good to be with Mother Barat.

"Oh, I wish you would stay in Rome always and always —couldn't you live here, Mother?" she pleaded.

Mother Barat looked at the eager little face and shook her head.

"Perhaps one day the time may come for the Mother-House to be here, but it can't be yet."

"Why not, Mother?" Giulia persisted.

Mother Barat remembered with a pang the sufferings she had endured for four years, after some of her council had wanted her in 1839 to govern the Society from Rome.

"Well, dear", she explained, "the French bishops don't like it, and the idea has got into some people's heads that it would mean altering other things as well."

Margherita turned to her.

"Mother, it's true, isn't it, that Gregory XVI has approved this year the very same constitution and rules that Leo XII approved, the ones that you and Father Varin drew up at Chevroz?"

"Yes, thank God", Mother Barat answered.

"When I spoke three years ago to my uncle the Cardinal about entering the Society", the girl went on, "he asked me, 'Do you want to glorify the Sacred Heart?' And when I said that was the only aim I had, he said, 'Wait then. There are some of the Reverend Mothers who want to change things and make the Society more and more like the Jesuits, and who think that it exists for the greater glory of God, and not especially to make Our Lord's great love known, but their foundress knows better, and so do her companions of the early days. They will wait and pray, and the Society will in the end go forward stronger than ever!'"

"He said you had—longanimity——" Giulia put in, "and when I asked him what that was, he said something I'd have to get hold of if I meant to be a saint, too."

"Well, now, all those who thought differently have come to see alike—one heart and one mind in the Heart of Jesus", Mother Barat said softly. "It is a keen suffering, Margherita, that comes to us from good people who think they are serving God, but He is not offended, and His Will has prevailed."

"Weren't four years a dreadfully long time to wait?" Margherita asked.

"They seem short now", Mother Barat replied. "And Our Lady stood beside us. When opinions were divided I went to her picture in the Villa Lante—you know the one—where she sits with the crown of thorns of her Son—and there I confided the problem to Our Lady of Sorrows. She was our safeguard."

"Look!" Giulia pointed down to the square below. "There are some people coming to see our picture of Mater Admirabilis—they're getting to know she gives us things." She turned sparkling eyes to the Mother General. "I know Our Lady loves you, and approves you like Margherita says the Pope does."

"Bless the child! Has she had a special revelation? The Junior School are so conceited since they helped Mother Perdrau to paint the fresco in the cloister", Margherita laughed.

Giulia tossed her head with decision.

"Oh, I know all about approval since we did that painting of Our Lady in the Temple. First of all it was, 'What on earth can a pack of youngsters do to help a painter? They'll spill the paint on themselves and spoil the job.' But we didn't, and Mother Perdrau approved our work, and so you all had to keep quiet. Then it was some of the nuns. Fancy putting Our Lady in a pink dress—whoever heard of such a thing? But she was *our* Madonna, and we like pink dresses, and she only wanted our approval. And then it was the bishop who was shocked with her curl—but all the people who come to pray to her don't mind that, and they approve of her. And then Our Lady says, I'll show you all now that I approve of the whole thing, and so she starts giving us graces, and she'll end by working miracles, see if she doesn't, and then I won't have to have a special revelation to say Our Lady approves you, will I, Mother Barat? It's just common sense."

Mother Barat laughed. Margherita quickly said:

"I hope you will approve of me when I am a novice, Mother. I think I shall have plenty of faults."

"The Sacred Heart burns up all our faults in a furnace of love, my dear child", Mother Barat told her. "Only love Him generously."

"When I am a novice", Giulia announced, "I shall try not to have any faults."

"Before you light the fire of the love of God, Giulia", Mother Barat warned, "be sure you sweep the chimney to get rid of the soot of pride."

They were interrupted by the sound of a heavy tread on the stairs.

"Ooh! Perhaps the dog has found you, Mother", Giulia said in delighted expectation. It was not, however, the shaggy head of the watchdog that appeared, but the round, rosy face of the farm sister. Panting, she came out on to the roof and burst forth, "Ah! Mother, there you are, and I thought I should never find you. Such a tragedy, poor dear, and I don't know what to do—I don't think perhaps I ought to tell you, but there, what else is there to do, and the poor thing is likely to die at any moment." She paused for breath.

"What is it?" Mother Barat asked her. "Let us know, and perhaps we can help."

"Oh dear!" Sister Agnes was almost in tears. "You know Bichette, the little white kid? The donkey got loose in the stable last night, and must have kicked her soundly. When I went in this morning, poor Bichette was lying in her corner looking for all the world like a dead animal. I've done my best with her, but she just won't touch anything to eat—oh dear, oh dear."

"Come, children." Mother Barat was off down the stairs so quickly that Giulia and Margherita had to run. They followed her through the garden to the shed.

"Bichette!" she called softly, and the kid answered with a plaintive bleat. Mother Barat turned to Sister Agnes, who had caught them up.

"Go quickly, and get some meal and some milk", she said, and when it came, she put some in the hollow of her hand. Bichette opened her eyes, her soft little tongue came out, and the food disappeared.

"Let me give her some", Giulia asked, but Bichette shut her eyes and bleated piteously.

"It's you she wants, Mother", said Margherita, and Mother Barat took some more of the mixture into her hand. Bichette's tongue came out again, and soon the meal was ended.

"Well, she won't eat for me", commented Sister Agnes.

"Very well, I'll come and feed her when she needs it.
Now good-bye. I have letters to write."

The Mother General was off into the house again. But
Giulia lingered with Sister Agnes.

"Sister", she asked, "how does God show He approves
of a saint?"

"Oh, that's an easy question to answer—He lets the
saint work some miracles, and then everyone knows—
that's the easiest way of doing it."

"Sister", Giulia went on, "have you ever seen Mother
Barat work a miracle?"

Sister Agnes was not surprised at the question.

"Well, not with my very own eyes, but when I was in
Turin, there was a child ill with fever. Mother Barat was
journeying to Rome, but we didn't know she was in the
house or even in the neighbourhood—it was to be kept a
secret. But bless me, if she didn't nearly give the whole
show away herself. Up she goes to the school infirmary and
finds the little girl. 'It's Mother Madeleine come to bless
you in the name of the Lord', she said, and made a little
cross on the child's forehead."

"And then what happened?" Giulia asked.

"Why, the fever left her, and she was as right as rain in
a couple of days, and going about telling everybody that
Madame Madeleine had cured her."

"Do you know any more stories, Sister?" Giulia's eyes
were big with wonder.

"Well, one of the mothers at the Villa told me she once
went into the room where Mother Barat was praying, and
there was a bright light shining from her." Sister Agnes
stopped and looked down at Giulia. "But you and I
don't want miracles, do we, to tell us that Mother Barat
is a saint? When I was ill at one time, she was too, and would
you believe it, she climbed all the way upstairs on her

knees to my room to see that I was all right. When a Mother General does things like that, you just know here", Sister Agnes thumped her broad chest, "that you've got hold of a saint."

Giulia nodded with understanding.

"Sister", she said solemnly, "that's what all the Junior School say—we just know."

Chapter XVII

BUSHELS AND CANDLESTICKS

MOTHER BARAT's carriage pulled up in front of the door that led to the noviceship at Conflans, and she went quickly in. The Mistress of Health met her at the entrance, with an anxious face.

"Oh, Mother", she said, "I am so glad you have come. The doctors went back to Paris half an hour ago."

"And what do they say?" Mother Barat too was anxious.

"They say there is no reasonable hope left for our poor little novice. The abscess on the brain is causing her excruciating pain. They have gone back to the Hôtel-Dieu to get their surgical instruments for an operation—it may relieve the agony she is in, though they can hardly think of saving her life."

"When will they return?"

"Not till tomorrow", the Mistress of Health answered. "I thought she could be given the Last Sacraments now. She is paralysed all down her left side, and the right side is painful. We have put ice on her head, but I think that in spite of the stabs of suffering, she is still conscious, though she cannot speak properly."

"Thank God", Mother Barat said. "In that case she can also make her vows, and die, if God wills, a member of the Society of His Sacred Heart. Tell the other novices to pray for her—they can go from the chapel with the Blessed Sacrament to the infirmary."

Mother Barat went straight up herself to the room where her sick daughter was lying—"O, Sacred Heart of Jesus," she prayed as she mounted the stairs, "wilt Thou take her from us when there is so much need here on earth for apostles of Thy love? Lord, she whom Thou lovest is sick."

The bell summoned the novices to the chapel at three o'clock. The sacristan had prepared candles for them to carry, and the white-veiled group knelt down the middle aisle while the priest unlocked the Tabernacle and took out the Ciborium.

"It's queer how big things depend on little accidents", thought Mother Perdrau. "Just a little knock, a small bruise, and now Sister de Monestrol is standing on the threshold of heaven. Do I envy her? To be on the point of going to Our Lord—that's glorious—but to stay here on earth to work for Him, well, that's glorious too."

She rose from her knees with the others, and the procession started up the stairs to the infirmary. Within the sickroom Mother Barat awaited the coming of Jesus of Nazareth, who had gone about healing the sick and giving life to the dead.

"Lord, she whom Thou lovest is sick", the cry rose from her heart torn with a mother's anguish. But He gave no sign.

On the stairs the novices waited patiently with their lighted candles. Mother Perdrau watched the flame eating down the wick as the minutes passed. The flame flickered in a draught that caught it, but it righted itself to steadiness again, and still the wax imperceptibly decreased. "This is like Sister de Monestrol's life", she thought. "Or like all our lives—they will burn out like a candle one of these days—I should like to be like this candle, burning out before the Blessed Sacrament." The draught came again suddenly, and she put up her hand quickly to shelter the flame. "Saved it that time", she said, and then "I wish we could save Sister de Monestrol—I wish there was a hand that could shelter her. Oh dear, here I am day-dreaming, and Mother Barat asked us to pray." She went back to her prayers as the door opened, and the priest came out again, his ministry ended.

A little later, four novices were coming down the stairs on their way to do housework, stepping on tiptoe for fear of making any noise. Mother Perdrau turned with her finger to her lips as they reached the end of the landing that led to the infirmary.

Suddenly the door of the sickroom opened quickly, and Mother Barat came running out, her face flushed and agitated.

"She looks almost scared", thought Mother Perdrau. "I've never seen her like that before."

Mother Barat called to her novices.

"Quick", she said in hurried, startled tones. "Go quickly to the altar of St. Philomena, and make a vow to her on my behalf. Tell her that if Sister de Monestrol gets better, for a whole year a novice will make a weekly communion in her honour, and we will have a lamp burning before her statue."

She turned away and disappeared from their surprised gaze, but, like good novices, they went off to the altar of St. Philomena and did as they were told.

It was just before night recreation, and Mother Perdrau was stifling a large yawn. Thank God there was bed at the end of a hardworking day! Only half an hour more, and then—when her thoughts had reached that pleasant prospect of white sheets and dreamless slumbers—she was called by a Professed nun: "Mother Barat wants to see you." Yawns were forgotten—Mother Perdrau walked as fast as religious decorum permitted—anything to get some precious minutes with the Mother General. She tapped

at her door. Mother Barat looked at her over her spectacles
with an inscrutable air.

"Pauline", she said in even tones, "your good health will
let us allow you to sit up during the night with Sister de
Monestrol—who is—better. I count on your keeping a
discreet silence between the two of you—she is a bit
over-excited—you'd better sleep in an armchair near
her."

Mother Perdrau opened her mouth to say something,
and then, seeing the look of reserve on Mother Barat's face,
she thought it wiser to ask no questions, and to make no
comments. Perhaps there were hopes now that Sister de
Monestrol would live.

After the greater silence had settled on the household,
Mother Perdrau quietly opened the door of the sickroom.
The Mistress of Health pointed to an armchair that had
been set so that she could watch the invalid, and then crept
out. Pauline sat down, and by the light of the lamp
turned low, she studied the sick novice. She seemed to be
sleeping with steady breathing; then her eyes beneath the
bandage on her head opened—was it the effect of the
lamplight, or did they twinkle with amusement? "Mother
Perdrau", the voice sounded quite firm, "I'm a bit un-
comfortable. They've left the ice on my head, and it's
freezing me. Could you take it off? I think I could sleep
then."

"What had I better do?" Pauline asked herself. "Well,
I was told to look after my sister—perhaps it won't hurt
her to have the ice taken away." It seemed to do her good.
Sister de Monestrol soon was really fast asleep; and so
peacefully that Mother Perdrau's nodding head gave up
the task of keeping watch and ward, and she too fell
asleep.

Some time later she awoke with a start. Heavens! She
had been asleep at her post with a dying sister—what had

happened to rouse her? Why, Sister de Monestrol was calling her again.

"Mother Perdrau", she said, and there was an embarrassed laugh behind her words, "I'm just dying of hunger—for heaven's sake get me something to eat."

"What?" Mother Perdrau was astonished. So this was what Mother Barat meant when she had said the novice was better. Perhaps it would not hurt her to have something to eat. She looked round the room. Ah, there was a little broth left there for the invalid. She took it over to Sister de Monestrol. Sitting upright in bed, she shook her head vigorously.

"You don't understand", she said. "I'm cured—really cured. It was our holy Mother who did it. She came into the room and made the sign of the cross on my forehead, which was burning hot. I knew she was praying. My head sank on to her hand, and then it was just as if boiling water was poured all over me. I suddenly felt my head was better, the paralysis left my side, and I could move again, and I cried out, 'But I can see everything—I can see the horizon through my window, and I can talk once more.' I think our Mother was overwhelmed. She just escaped out of the room as quickly as she could."

Light dawned on Mother Perdrau.

"Ah! That must have been when she came upon us on the stairs, and asked us to go and make a vow to St. Philomena—to try to give her the credit for the miracle."

"Oh, St. Philomena has enough to her credit already", said Sister de Monestrol. "This is our Mother Barat's, and I'll see to it that, in spite of her humility, people know that she has worked this miracle. But the marvellous thing at the moment is my appetite. I shall die if you can't give me something more substantial than broth to eat."

"Good", answered Pauline. "I was told to look after you." She crept downstairs and discovered some cold chicken in a cupboard. At the bottom of the bread-basket there was some bread that was not too dry. She caught sight of a bottle of wine—that would complete the feast, and triumphantly she crept upstairs again. It was not an elegant meal to tempt a sick person's appetite, but Sister de Monestrol did not seem to mind. Chicken and bread disappeared speedily, amid suppressed laughter.

"What do you feel like now?" Mother Perdrau asked.

"Oh, just as if I had had a bad headache. I'm all right, but I'm bothered about Mother Barat. She will try to get out of the miracle. I have an idea. Get out that writing-desk, and your pen and ink. There's paper over there. Now I'll tell you all the details, and you will write them down, and then we'll both sign them, and there will be a legal document to prove things."

Busily they set to work, and when the dawn of a new day reddened the sky, two signatures attested the facts of the cure.

Seriously three doctors drew up in the early morning outside the house, and walked up to the infirmary with their instruments. They went into the sickroom and rubbed their eyes.

"But this is not the same person as she was yesterday", they cried as they saw the smiling novice. "There's no question of an operation. She's as well as we are. We'll join you in thanksgiving to God, who has brought this cure about."

When they were gone, Mother Barat went to her daughter. Not a word did she say about her part in the miracle.

"God has been good to you", she said. "You owe Him a great debt. I know of only one coinage to repay Him with— Don't set any limits to your love of His Sacred Heart and of His Cross."

She bent over and made a little cross on her forehead.

Sister de Monestrol felt the last bit of headache disappear. She did not dare to make any reference to her gratitude to Mother Barat, but she thought within: "Ah, it's all very well trying to put a bushel over the candle of your holiness, but when God wants it, He'll set you up on a candlestick, and then we'll have our witness ready. . . ."

Mr. John Tyrrell of the British Embassy sat in the parlour of the Hôtel Biron on July 21st, 1849, and waited for his daughter. He put down the review of J. S. Mill's *Logic* which he had been reading in the *Edinburgh*, and thought, "It's strange what a long time it takes for people to become really rational, to learn to believe only those things that they can prove and to trust only the evidence of their own eyes. They will still cling to the idea that there is a supernatural world, in spite of all that is being written nowadays to show them the contrary. I wonder if I am wise in sending Rita to school here. I know she gets a training that fits her to take her place in society, I know that she is taught to appreciate good books and culture, but there is still a residue of superstition that may influence her, even though I have always taught her that the world is real only in so far as we can see and hear and handle it and grasp it as a material thing through our senses."

He was interrupted by the arrival of his daughter, who sat down beside him, smiling with the pleasure of the visit.

"Well, Rita", he said, admiring the good looks of his fifteen year old daughter, "I hope you are working well—and enjoying life."

"Oh, yes, father", said Rita and meant it. "It's grand just now. We're going to wish Mother Barat a happy feast to-morrow—it's St. Mary Magdalen's feastday, and her name is Madeleine, you know, and we're having a kind of play for her, and we all think she is going to like it ever so much."

"And how is Mother Barat? She always strikes me as such a sensible woman."

"Father, she's more than sensible—she's holy." Rita saw her father's eyebrows go up in sceptical amusement.

"I know she's sensible too", she added hastily. "I mean she knows just what to do practically—like last year when there were the revolutionaries fighting all round us again, and she kept us playing noisy games like hide-and-seek, so that we never knew there was any danger until she had somewhere safe for us all to go to, and I suppose it was common sense to let the ruffians in to the courtyard, and to get on their right side by giving them a decent meal— but you know there's something else they recognised besides just common sense and good nature."

Mr. Tyrrell looked at his daughter seriously. "Rita," he said, "Mother Barat is a remarkable woman, with a mind above the ordinary, with a width of view and culture that is unusual. She has gifts of character and heart that I can recognise and appreciate, but I don't make the mistake that I think you are doing, of attributing them to some supernatural influence. They are all quite natural— you mustn't allow yourself to pick up any Catholic super-stitions about there being a God who has special dealings with saints. Use your brain and your reason, my dear, and don't believe anything that you cannot see for yourself."

"But how can you see the supernatural?" Rita asked, somewhat puzzled.

"Ah, that is the point", her father replied. "You can't ever see the supernatural—I have never seen the super-natural—therefore there is no supernatural. That is just what I wanted you to understand." His words rather took the spirit out of what she was going to tell him of the entertainment for Mother Barat—he wouldn't like the idea. Perhaps it was a bit silly.

However, the next day she was ready to admire the long lines of schoolgirls in their white dresses sitting in the assembly hall ready for the arrival of the Mother General.

When Mother Barat had taken her place in the middle of the top end, with the children stretching down on each side of her, the curtains at the far end parted and showed a road that wound uphill. Three of the girls were dressed allegorically as Faith, Hope and Charity, and as they spoke they pointed to the summit of the hill, where a large representation of the Sacred Heart seemed to glow and flame with hidden lights. Earth was a place of exile, the fresh young voices cried, but Paradise drew us where Our Lord's Sacred Heart was on fire with love of us.

"I wish I believed that", Rita thought sadly. "It is very lovely, but Father would say it's only a fairy-tale without any reality. The Heart there burns with firework flares—I can prove that, but how could I touch the burning love that Mother Barat believes in?"

She stopped puzzling, for the performance was over, and the school waited for Mother Barat to say the customary words of appreciation of their work. There was silence. The Mother General said nothing. She sat absolutely still, her hands joined as though she was praying, her eyes fixed on the Sacred Heart. The headmistress of the school turned to her after a pause.

"Mother", she said, "the children are very pleased to have been able to wish you a happy feast."

Still Mother Barat said nothing. Her gaze drank in something that others could not see. The hush that lay around her spread to the children. Motionless they looked at her. She wasn't ill—she looked too happy—but why didn't she talk to them? She didn't seem to notice they were there, even. What was happening?

The headmistress waited a little longer, then raising her voice, said simply, "Mother Barat wants to pray to the Heart of Jesus that you have spoken about so beautifully. Lead out, children."

The noise of the departing school did not disturb the

Mother General's contemplation. Presently the sisters arrived and began to take down the stands and decorations and dismantle the room. Still she remained absorbed in her prayer. At the end of three quarters of an hour she came to herself. She was alone in the hall with a few of the older mothers. There was no mistaking the fact that God had made a public exhibition of her. "What a trick I've been played", she said, and made for the shelter of her room.

"Mother Perdrau!" Rita had caught someone who could answer her question. "What happened to Mother Barat? I can't explain it myself, but I saw with my own eyes that she was seeing something that I couldn't see, and that she was held so still by something that I couldn't feel, and that there was a happiness that was, well, eating her up without her being able to stop it. What was it, Mother Perdrau?"

"Our Lord", said Mother Perdrau unhesitatingly. "We showed her the symbol, but then the reality seized her. Our Lord was showing her a little of what you and I will only see when we are in heaven—God does do that to His saints sometimes. We put artificial lights round a picture of His Sacred Heart, and then He said, 'Look, Mother Barat is a real light that burns in your midst.' People like her, you know, Rita, light up our world, and make some of our ideas appear a little silly—especially when we think we are being very reasonable."

K

Chapter XVIII

WHO IS MY NEIGHBOUR?

MOTHER BARAT sat down at her desk and took the top letter from a pile that lay ready for answering. She sighed as she read it through. "Poor Julia," she thought, "will she never learn to curb that fierce temper of hers? She has thrown up her work again. Well, I shall just have to give her shelter once more—if we don't nobody else will."

She began an answer, her quill pen moving swiftly to and fro across the paper. The little grey cat at her feet found it fascinating to watch. With a light bound he was on her table, stretched out beside her, his paw patting on the feather each time it passed him by. She smiled down at the lithe form, but did not pause in her work until the last word was written. There came a knock at the door, and Mother Perdrau entered with a child of three years toddling beside her.

"Mother," she said, "I've brought our latest pupil to see you—Louise arrived last night—her mother finds entertaining takes all her time, and we are to look after the baby."

Suspecting a rival, the little grey cat leaped on to the window ledge. "Ooh, pussy!" said Louise, and left the safety of Mother Perdrau's skirts. The cat took no notice of her. Louise turned to inspect the rest of the room. She gravely surveyed Mother Barat, her white cap frill, her shining cross, her long black rosary, then up again her eyes travelled to the eyes that were watching her as carefully. At once her mind was made up. With a rush she flung herself into Mother Barat's arms and snuggled up against her, looking out from her vantage point at all the world with confidence.

"How can a mother be parted from a child like this!" Mother Barat exclaimed. "It isn't moral or Christian. Poor little thing!—to be abandoned to the care of servants while the parents go off to theatres and dances—I bless our vocation that we can be like mothers to them when their own do not care—that we can give happiness to these little innocents. Oh, Mother Perdrau, we must respect all children and honour their souls made in the image of God. Let them know that we love them."

She offered a sweet to Louise. One baby hand held it while the other patted Mother Barat's cheeks.

"I like you", said Louise solemnly, and cast many a backward glance as Mother Perdrau led her away.

Mother Barat began on the next letter. There was another knock at the door. The portress came in.

"Mother", she announced, "the Bishop is waiting for you in the parlour." Mother Barat rose at once.

"And the policeman was here", the portress added, "to complain of the behaviour of three of our girls."

"What have they been doing?" The Mother General was a little alarmed.

"He says that the other day when the police were at dinner in their office across the road, these girls came out laughing so heartily that it disturbed their meal", the sister said.

Mother Barat threw back her head and laughed too.

"Well, Mother, I'm glad you don't think the end of the world is coming when we get into trouble for our hilarity", the sister commented as she went back to the lodge.

Her interview over, the Mother General came out with his Lordship the Bishop. As soon as she appeared at the door, an old man stepped forward, and disregarding the presence of the Bishop, cried, "Ah, Mother Barat, I've been waiting to see you. Just look at these lovely new boots I've got with the money you gave me."

He held out a pair of large hobnailed boots. Mother Barat took them into her own hands, turned them this way and that, with a masterly eye on their good points.

"Yes, they're a good pair", she told him approvingly.

"She knows a good thing when she sees it", the man told the Bishop confidentially, and went off delighted.

The portress was waiting again when the Bishop had gone.

"Colonel Hervé is in the other parlour—he's brought his little daughter, too."

It was a meeting of old friends.

"Madame", the colonel said, "I wish we could have you again staying in Alsace. Do you remember the time when you were ill there, and we had you for a nice long time?"

"I remember", said Mother Barat smiling. "I remember you had the goodness to pull me in my little wheeled chair, and you said, 'It's a rare thing to see a colonel leading a general'."

"I was more proud of pulling you than of being at the head of my regiment", he said, and added, "Here's my daughter—she wants to ask you for a piece of advice that you have found useful yourself, madame."

Mother Barat looked at the eager face of the young girl. As though she were talking to an equal, she said, "Every morning say, 'Today, Lord, I will begin to love You and serve You. May this day be wholly Yours and for You. And may I find when night comes that I have known and loved and served You a little better.' That is what I say and you will find it brings you peace and strength and consolation."

Then how many questions there were to ask about the

rest of the family! "Don't you ever forget anybody?" the colonel asked, laughing, as he said goodbye.

Up in her room again Mother Barat turned to her letters.

"We haven't got Californian gold mines", she thought ruefully as she dealt with the financial difficulties of an American house, "but we'll do our best to help."

"How good God was", she pondered as she read the next letter. It ran, "I shall never thank God enough that I chanced to meet you that day on the road to Marmoutier. You must have broken your journey and inconvenienced yourself badly, I see now, but you stopped me from sinning deeply. I meant to give up my faith and everything—and then you came along and talked to me, and I remembered how happy I had been at your school, and when you were kind to me as you used to be, why, then I saw how God would be hurt if I left Him, since you were so heartbroken at the idea." "It would have been worth while founding the Society if that one soul alone was saved", Mother Barat thought.

There came another knock at the door. The mistress-general of the boarding school entered.

"Mother, the girls are looking forward to seeing you this afternoon—will you be able to come?"

"Of course I can—and please see that they have a good tea—and I shall not have the heart not to see the Junior School just for a wee minute——" Mother Barat smiled at the prospect and took up her pen again. The portress knocked and came in with a tale of woe.

"Mother, there's a poor washerwoman—her husband drinks—she works in a place where they don't pay her regularly—she's dreadfully poor—she comes here and gets soup, which she carries away in her basket to her four little children—she says they have their mouths open like little sparrows to get a mouthful from the Sacred Heart."

Before the tale was ended, Mother Barat was up and searching in her cupboard.

"Here, quick", she cried, "take these warm clothes to the poor woman—and these vests to the children—this little coat would do for one of them, wouldn't it?"

"Mother," protested the portress, "these things are too good."

"What?" Mother Barat turned round like lightning. "Too good for the poor? I would give them my very skin. I've no coat for the mother—I must give the woman my cloak."

"Mother", the portress reminded her, "you gave it away yesterday. Can I give mine?"

"And now", Mother Barat added, "be off to the kitchen and get the cooks to give you a really large beakful of food for the little birds."

She sat down to her letters again, but soon the door opened to admit the sister infirmarian.

"Mother, Dr. Récamier said you were to have your dinner in your room", she said, and placed a tray beside her. "And he told me to say that as you can't be stopped spending so much time in that cold little tribune saying your prayers, he has provided a stove and fuel for it, and he says you must take it, as *he* hasn't made a vow of poverty."

Before she began her dinner, Mother Barat finished the letter she was writing, and addressed it. "Eugénie de Smet[1]," she said, "there's an ardent soul for you! What a privilege to have taught her—I wonder what God has in store for her."

The noise of voices raised in cheerful conversation came to her and she looked out of her window. The workmen engaged on repairs were having their meal just outside. One old man was alone, standing behind an elm tree. She watched him take a piece of dry bread from his pocket.

[1] She was the foundress of the Helpers of the Holy Souls.

The others were pulling out sausages and bottles of wine and cheese. Mother Barat went to her tray, took up the roll and cut it in two. Then she spread the meat they had given her between the slices and closed the sandwich, wrapped it up in a piece of paper, and rang the bell. The portress appeared.

"Please, sister, take this packet to the old man under the tree there."

The Mother General watched her dinner disappear with great delight. Later the Infirmarian took away the tray with great delight, too.

"It really looks as if our Mother was getting an appetite", she thought.

Mother Barat was summoned to the parlour again. An old lady was seated wrapped up in a fur coat, her silk bonnet expressing disapproval with its nodding feather as she raised her lorgnette with a bejewelled hand and looked at the little nun who entered.

"Mother Barat", she said, "I have come to complain of what you are teaching my small granddaughter. Last week it was her tenth birthday, and I wanted to give her pleasure. I gave her a new dress and cape—a beautiful colour—the very latest shade of auricula—and a charming little pink plush hat to go with it, and do you know what she said?" The old lady bridled indignantly at the recollection. Mother Barat shook her head.

"Well, if you please, she said, 'Grannie, thank you very much, but you ought to have consulted me first, and I should have asked you for some sand.' Some sand! What are things coming to when I am expected to give my little Julie sand for a present?" The bonnet nodded its feather with recollected annoyance.

Mother Barat looked at her. What a pity her warm heart for her grandchild could not find a wise way of expressing itself, but could only imagine frivolous pleasures.

"I have heard about this sand", she said softly. "It was a plot of the Junior School that they hatched all on their own. They had noticed that they, who had warm furred boots, had a playground covered with sand that dried quickly, whereas the children of the poor school play about on an earthen playground that is very damp indeed. They said to each other, 'It isn't fair that the poor children, who have shoes with holes in them, should have to squelch about—we'll see to it that they have sand too.' We knew nothing about it until they had planned to collect themselves for it, but don't you think that the Heart of Our Lord was pleased to see this act of charity that reconciles the poor with the rich?"

The feather of the bonnet had stopped nodding. The lorgnette was still helping the old lady to look at Mother Barat, but the eyes behind the glass were a little moist.

"Mother Barat", she said at length, "I hadn't thought of it in that way." She fumbled in her reticule and drew out some gold pieces.

"May I buy some of the sand?" she asked.

Mother Barat smiled. "I shall tell Julie myself", she said. "How pleased she will be!"

On her way to the school she passed one of the old sisters. She stopped her and touched her shawl.

"My poor sister", she said, "what a thin shawl!—and have you a woollen petticoat? Why, it's as thin as a piece of lace. Come along with me." She led her to her room and took out one of her own.

"Now, sister, we'll exchange, and you'll be like a marquess. Ah, sister, you don't know what a joy it is for us to help you—you are so like Our Lord. While we are teaching and writing, you are helping St. Joseph and Our Lady in the house at Nazareth; like Jesus you are sweeping the room and peeling the vegetables, because Mary is lighting the fire to cook them. How I wish I were you!"

Old Sister Agnes broke in. "Well, Mother, if I were in your place, since you are Mother General and can arrange things, I should once and for all make myself into a sister, and that would settle the question."

She watched the Mother General make off towards the school and shook her head.

"I doubt it's a bit too late now when she's getting on for eighty", she sighed. "But she'd have made a very good sister."

A burst of happy laughter came from the school hall, where the older girls were meeting Mother Barat.

"Ah," commented Sister Agnes, "and she's made a better teacher."

She gathered up the warm petticoat.

"But I think best of all, she's made a good mother", she said, as she hobbled off to her work.

Chapter XIX

HEAVEN ON THURSDAY

LAVINIA was a lively little American. Her grandmother had been one of Mother Duchesne's first pupils in the old log cabin in Missouri, her mother had been to the school newly opened in New York, and here she was, at the age of nine, under the wide-spreading cedar tree in the garden at Paris, on this sunny afternoon in early May, actually talking and listening to Mother Barat.

"How funny—Grandmamma could have seen her, and Mother could have seen her, but they didn't, and I am seeing her—Mother Perdrau says she's eighty-five—what a long time to live—well, I'm a lucky person to be here. It's lovely being with Mother Barat." Lavinia hugged her knees as she sat on the outskirts of the little group of Junior School children gathered round the Mother General and wriggled with pleasure. She watched Adèle go up and whisper some secret in Mother Barat's ear, while sitting right up against her on the ground, tiny Louise scooped her hand across the black skirts of her habit and then poured what she had gathered out over her own dress.

"Look at Louise", Mathilde whispered to Lavinia. "She's scooping up Mother Barat's holiness. I wish I could, but she would notice me, and Mother Perdrau says she hates us to think she is a saint. Did you get any of the straw from her chair the other day? I did, and three of the big girls wanted me to give it to them, but I want to keep it myself—for my descendants, you know, as a relic like the ones in the chapel."

"I didn't get any", said Lavinia sadly.

"Never mind", Mathilde counselled. "Slip up now and get a bit of her shawl fringe."

They were interrupted by the arrival of two sisters with baskets.

"I won't count you", laughed Mother Barat. "I said I would see twenty of you——"

"We're twenty-nine", thought Lavinia.

"—and I don't want to find I have one too many", added Mother Barat. "Now, sisters, hand round the apples and the cakes. Come, children, get your teeth into them—that's your first job—I have some more for the others, so set to. Keep the cakes for your tea. I wanted to see you first before the others, because you are going to make your First Communion."

The apples were fast disappearing. The band of children crept closer to Mother Barat, just looking at her and listening to her as she spoke to them of the things of God in her gentle, quiet voice. "And now we shall have to say goodbye to each other," she said at last, "but you must promise me to say every night to God, 'Give me grace to die rather than offend You by mortal sin'."

The children nodded, catching some glimpse of what sin is as they felt her love go out to them. She went on: "Sin—what do you think of sin which wounds the Heart of Jesus and which stops us from going to God when we die? Where God is not, there is Hell."

"How awful!" said Lavinia. "Sin is just awful!"

"I'll try never to sin—not even a little teeny sin", cried Mathilde.

"I'll tell you what I'll do", Adèle said. "Every night I'll put my heart to soak in the Immaculate Heart of Our Lady, and then in the morning I'll just have to take it out, and it'll be quite fresh and quite clean to receive Our Lord —and then there won't be any room for sin."

"Fancy being separated from God for ever and ever", added Lavinia. "Why, I hated it this winter when we didn't see you for so long, Mother Barat."

Their protestations were serious, and Mother Barat smiled with joy at the sight of so many ready to please the Lord for whom she had worked so long. The promised hundredfold was appearing already.

"That is right, my dear children", she said, "and then we shall all see each other again in the beauty of heaven, where we shall be with Our Lady as well, for ever and ever."

"Oh Mother", said Louise, and clasped Mother Barat's knees in silence and sheer delight at so happy a future.

"When can the others come along to see you?" Lavinia asked, as she thought of the treat they were missing.

Mother Barat looked at her.

"My dear", she said quickly, "what did you come here to see? Something very little and very imperfect——" she broke off as the whole band raised their voices in protest. "Let's go and see the grotto and the statue where St. Mary Magdalen is meeting Our Lord after His Resurrection." She rose, but the children fell on their knees. As she raised her hand to bless them, Mother Barat thought, "Such open innocent faces—God is in their hearts. What a reward for all our labours, what an encouragement to love our vocation more and more—this long life of mine looks to me like a dream compared with eternity—where we shall all meet again." She made the sign of the cross over the silent bowed heads. "Crosses will come", she pondered, "but they will be our delight. Our Lord will carry them with us and take from them their bitterness."

The children got up and went off, turning again to wave to her as she stood beneath the cedar tree with the spring sunlight golden through the branches.

Lavinia and Mathilde stopped as they reached the little green door that led back from the Mother-House garden to the school.

"Wasn't it lovely to be with her!" Lavinia sighed. "I wonder what we'll be like when we're as old as she is. Scratchy old ladies with a parrot."

"And a poodle", said Mathilde, "and worrying about the way they serve our bread and milk—unless of course we try to do the sort of things she wants us to. Oh Lavinia, we won't really be horrid because she'll tell us when we're going wrong——"

Lavinia was silent. She was wondering.

"But will she always be there to tell us?" she asked.

Mathilde turned on her quickly.

"Of course—if she's not here, she'll be in heaven, and you don't suppose she'll forget us there, do you?"

"No." Lavinia was quite positive. "I think she's a bit like the cedar tree—she sort of spreads out her branches, and we all go and shelter underneath, and we get on with our jobs and forget about the tree, but it's there all the time, giving us its shade."

"And we're going to see her again on Ascension Day when we've made our First Communion", Mathilde added, with a smile of pleasure at the prospect. "She's promised us that. It's only a fortnight more to wait."

For the nuns the fortnight seemed to pass very quickly. Mother Barat was full of renewed vigour now that the warm weather was covering the trees with green and making the skies blue. She came and went among them with the gaiety they loved so much, speaking to them of the virtues so dear to Our Lord's Sacred Heart.

"I am always repeating myself", she told them, "and harping on the same string, but be humble—be very humble. You see, if this rung of the ladder of virtue is missing, you will never get to heaven."

The Sunday before Ascension Day she surprised every-one by going to the general recreation at midday.

"I was very anxious to come to see you all today", she said as she looked round at her daughters' faces beaming with the pleasure of seeing her, "for on Thursday we are going to heaven."

"It is a heavenly feast", thought Mother Perdrau. "On the first Ascension Day how the disciples' thoughts must have gone up into heaven with Our Blessed Lord, rejoicing that He was at last enjoying all its happiness. No wonder they had to have an angel to tell them to stop gazing up and to get on with the work He had given them to do on earth."

One of the nuns was reading out some letters from the little boys in the school at Marmoutier.

"Mother", she said, "here's one who hopes you will live for a long time still."

Mother Barat shook her head. "Give me the next one quickly", she said.

"Dear Mother Barat", the nun read out, "I hope you are quite well. I am praying that I shall meet you in heaven."

"Ah, I shall be pleased to see him there", Mother Barat commented. "One day we shall all be together in heaven. I hope for this from the Sacred Heart of Jesus, for all who love Him to the end."

The next day the First Communicants had begun their retreat. Mother Perdrau was taking them to the little chapel in the garden where the priest was to give them an instruction. Lavinia was counting the days as she walked along. "Monday, Tuesday, Wednesday, then Thursday— and Our Lord will come to me", she thought with awe. "It's more than just going to heaven—only I suppose I won't know how wonderful it is until I do really go to heaven—or until I'm like Mother Barat—sort of living with one foot inside."

Mother Perdrau was watching two of the servants from the Mother-House hurrying along to the gates. She stopped them for a second and asked, "What is the matter? Is anything wrong?"

The men showed anxious faces. "It's the Mother General", they said. "She's had an attack—we're off for the priest and the doctor."

How still and cold the great Mother-House seemed in the days that followed! Silent and motionless upon her bed lay the mother whose presence had always seemed to bring life to things around her. Now as the hours dragged by, the life in her seemed to grow fainter and fainter, and only a smile on her face and a pressure of her hand showed that her heart was still warm for those she loved on earth.

The First Communicants heard that she was ill and prayed for her. "She's had the Last Sacraments", Mother Perdrau told Lavinia, "but she can't receive Our Lord now."

Lavinia's eyes filled with tears. What a grief that must be for Mother Barat! Mother Perdrau looked down at the sad face beside her.

"Lavinia," she said, "I know I can trust you not to tell this to the others, but I think you will understand. This morning I had to watch in Mother Barat's room as soon as I had been to Holy Communion. You know, we are like a ciborium at that moment. I went to her bedside, and took her hand and placed it on my heart and whispered, 'He is there—Our Eucharistic Lord is visiting you—I have brought Him to you as I have just communicated.' You can't think how strongly her hand pressed immediately against my heart—so she did have the joy of Our Lord coming quite near to her."

Lavinia was silent—what could you say when happiness and sorrow ran together like the colours of a sunset?

Ascension Day dawned. Little by little the earth slipped

away from Mother Barat. Noonday softened into evening, and the light faded in the sky. The stars came out in the darkness. When the hands of the clock pointed to half past eleven, Mother Barat was with the Lord she had loved so long and so well.

The next day the First Communicants begged to be allowed to see her again.

"She promised us", they reminded Mother Perdrau. "She was going to give us another blessing."

"We want to go too", said the littlest children in the Junior School, and as they entered the room where she lay surrounded with flowers, they smiled to see their beloved mother again. Little Madeleine climbed up on a stool beside her and took up one of her cold hands and covered it with kisses. In their white dresses, with white rose crowns on their heads, the twenty-five First Communicants encircled her and prayed.

"It's like a peep into heaven", Lavinia thought, with confused recollections of the white-robed choirs that follow the Lamb. "I can't pray for her. I'm sure she is with Our Lord. Oh Mother Barat, don't forget me", she whispered and slipped a tiny bunch of violets that she had picked in the garden among the other flowers. The others were still praying. "Jesus, meek and humble of heart, make my heart like unto Thine," said Lavinia.

POSTSCRIPT

Corporal Mary Smith of the A.T.S. shut the door behind her and sat on the edge of her bed.

"Heavens!" she thought, "whoever could have dreamed of spending Boxing Day in an R.C. convent— and enjoying it! Well, it's a treat to have a room to myself— and a treat to get a bit of quiet—there's a sort of comfortable quiet about the place even though we've been making noise enough." She laughed in recollection and then picked up a writing-pad from the table.

"I'd better give them a line at home", she said, and headed the sheet of notepaper:

> *Convent of the Sacred Heart,*
> *Jette St. Pierre,*
> *near Brussels.*
>
> *Boxing Day,* 1944.

"Dear Mum (she wrote),

"This is to wish you a very happy Christmas and hoping that you'll keep out of the way of bombs. You'd never guess where we've been billeted; it's a convent, of all places. You should have seen some of the girls' faces when they were told where they were to go—though I don't think they really thought they were in for the Inquisition and thumbscrews and cementing up in the walls. I think most of us thought we were just going to be dull as ditchwater, and having to mind our P's and Q's. But it has been great fun. There are several nuns here who speak English, so we get along fine. They say they have quite a lot of houses in England and Scotland and Ireland—actually four in

London—and I've lived there all my life without knowing it, and one is on Hammersmith Broadway, where we've often passed in the bus. Their H.Q. or Mother-House, as they call it, is in Rome, and there are convents in Italy, Spain, Germany, Poland, Austria, Holland and France. The Belgian nuns look after real blacks in the Congo, and there are schools in Egypt, India, China and Japan, Australia and New Zealand. We ran into some New Yorkers in Brussels who were thrilled to find we were in billets here—it seems they were old children of the nuns in America—two from New York, and one from a place in the south where a Mother Doochain or something went first of all to teach the Red Indians and to begin the houses in the States—they're all over Canada and South America, too."

She paused to listen to a flight of aeroplanes passing northward overhead, and then began again:

"They gave us a splendid Christmas-day dinner—I must say the sisters know how to cook—where they managed to get things from, I don't know, but they said they wanted to show their gratitude—they gave us beer and smokes and then showed us all sorts of things in the convent. They have a shrine there where their foundress is buried—her name is Saint Madeleine Sophie Barat. She was buried first at Conflans, which is near Paris, but the nuns were turned out of France about 1900 and moved her body. It's a curious thing, but the body is just as if she had only recently died; incorrupt, they called it. Some of the girls didn't believe that it wasn't embalmed or treated in some way, but they said that she had been buried like anyone else—and anyhow, I think it's queer that the limbs were still flexible when they first reopened her vault. The nuns seem to love her very much—she was only a cooper's daughter, they say, but all sorts of people like popes and princesses used to be her friends and ask her advice. She was Mother General for sixty-five years—I reckon that's enough to make a saint of anyone.

"One of the nuns told me she went with some children from her school to Rome in 1925 when the Pope declared her a saint. She said there were thousands and thousands of Children of the Sacred Heart from all over the world, all dressed in white, and lots of old grannies with white hair, wearing the pink and green and blue ribbons they won at school. She said you ought to have heard the cheers when the banner with her picture on it was carried into St. Peter's—they've got a big statue of her there now. She said she has met an old nun who was dying in 1882 when she was quite young, and they prayed to the saint and she cured her and she's lived getting on for sixty years more. So that's what prayers to saints can do!

"Well, Mum, you see you needn't worry about me at all. I forgot to say the nuns said they would pray for all our relations—that means you, and they seem to think that will help to keep you safe. So long.

Much love,
Mary."

She blotted the last words and folded the letter into an envelope. A knock came at the door.

"Entrez!" she called out, but it was one of the English-speaking nuns who looked in.

"I just came to see if you had everything you could want", she said. Corporal Smith sighed.

"Yes, thank you", she answered. "It's lovely here. You nuns are lucky, to be able to be so quiet and un-disturbed and unworried while we live in the hurly-burly of war and noise and bothers——"

The nun smiled.

"You make me think of a story of our Holy Mother.

She was travelling one day in a coach with a couple of carters, who said to her, 'You are very calm, while we have to put up with a lot of hardship.'

" 'I'm not at all calm', she replied, 'I've a lot of worries for myself and for others. So many people don't think about the next world, which will last for ever and ever. And what do you think about heaven and hell, my friends?' "

" 'Nothing at all', they answered. 'And are *you* bothered about them? Keep a stout heart.'

"Then she told them the story of two travellers who met a monk and said to him, 'You're a poor man who will be properly had if there isn't a paradise.' But the monk retorted, 'You will be even more had if there is a hell.' Then St. Madeleine Sophie pulled out her rosary and said, 'While I say this for you, think about things, so that we shan't have travelled together without finding ourselves at the journey's end for ever with God'."

The nun stopped.

"And then what happened?" Corporal Smith asked.

"They came to see her again—and in the end practised their religion", the nun concluded. "But I didn't come in to tell you stories when you ought to be in bed. I found this holy picture with some English writing on it, and I thought you might like it. Good-night."

She put the picture on the table and went out. Corporal Smith picked it up. It showed Jesus Christ baring His Heart, which was surrounded with flames, while He held out His hand, as though He were a beggar asking for alms. Underneath were the words, "My son, give Me your heart", and on the line below, as though in answer, "Jesus, meek and humble of heart, make my heart like unto Thine." Corporal Smith looked at it all the time she was undressing, and wondered what they would say at home if they could see her.

"I think I'll send it home", she thought. "Mum would like it—but I'd like to keep it myself, too."

Just before she climbed into bed, she pulled the blackout curtain aside and looked out into the dark night. Far to the north a red glow was starting in the sky.

"The bombers have got something there", she sighed. "My goodness, it's burning."

It was much too far away to see anything more than the reflection in the darkness that lay over everything, but, as she watched, the light grew and spread over more and more of the horizon.

"Fire's awful", Corporal Smith thought. "There's no stopping it once it's got a hold on things. How it's lighting up the whole sky! It looks almost as if it was the first red light of a new day dawning."

She climbed into bed and fell asleep. But the nun had gone to kneel beside the shrine, thoughts crowding into her mind. A new day to face, a new world to live in, a new age opening out with its dangers and difficulties and its unpredictable conflagrations. Would it always be, not peace but the sword? Short truces in a constant warfare? St. Madeleine Sophie, who lay now so peacefully before her, had known little quiet in her eighty-five years of life: the French Revolution, the conquests of Napoleon, the subversive troubles of 1830 and 1848, wars and rumours of wars throughout the world—yet they had all passed. God's love remained. What was it that the saint would say now before the uncertain future? "Courage and confidence; I can never repeat this war-cry too often: *Cor Jesu, in Te confido.*"